THE INTERNATIONAL ENCYCLOPEDIA OF PHYSICAL CHEMISTRY AND CHEMICAL PHYSICS

Topic 10. THE FLUID STATE

EDITOR: J. S. ROWLINSON

Volume 1

LATTICE THEORIES OF THE LIQUID STATE

THE INTERNATIONAL ENCYCLOPEDIA
OF PHYSICAL CHEMISTRY AND CHEMICAL PHYSICS

Members of the Honorary Editorial Advisory Board

THE INTERNATIONAL ENCYCLOPEDIA
OF PHYSICAL CHEMISTRY AND CHEMICAL PHYSICS

Editors-in-Chief

E. A. GUGGENHEIM
READING

J. E. MAYER
LA JOLLA

F. C. TOMPKINS
LONDON

Chairman of the Editorial Advisory Group

ROBERT MAXWELL

PUBLISHER AT PERGAMON PRESS

List of Topics and Editors

LATTICE THEORIES OF THE LIQUID STATE

BY

J. A. BARKER, B.A., D.Sc.

PRINCIPAL RESEARCH OFFICER
DIVISION OF PHYSICAL CHEMISTRY, C.S.I.R.O.
MELBOURNE, AUSTRALIA

PERGAMON PRESS

OXFORD · LONDON · NEW YORK · PARIS

1963

PERGAMON PRESS LTD.
Headington Hill Hall, Oxford
4 & 5 Fitzroy Square, London W.1

PERGAMON PRESS INC.
122 East 55th Street, New York, 22 N.Y.

GAUTHIER-VILLARS
55 Quai des Grands-Augustins, Paris 6

PERGAMON PRESS G.m.b.H.
Kaiserstrasse 75, Frankfurt am Main

Library of Congress Card No. 61–16896

*Set in Modern 7—11 on 13pt. by Santype Limited, Salisbury, and printed in
Great Britain by Cox and Wyman Ltd., Reading, Berkshire.*

INTRODUCTION

THE International Encylopedia of Physical Chemistry and Chemical Physics is a comprehensive and modern account of all aspects of the domain of science between chemistry and physics, and is written primarily for the graduate and research worker. The Editors-in-Chief, Professor E. A. GUGGENHEIM, Professor J. E. MAYER and Professor F. C. TOMPKINS, have grouped the subject matter in some twenty groups (General Topics), each having its own editor. The complete work consists of about one hundred volumes, each volume being restricted to around two hundred pages and having a large measure of independence. Particular importance has been given to the exposition of the fundamental bases of each topic and to the development of the theoretical aspects; experimental details of an essentially practical nature are not emphasized although the theoretical background of techniques and procedures is fully developed.

The Encyclopedia is written throughout in English and the recommendations of the International Union of Pure and Applied Chemistry on notation and cognate matters in physical chemistry are adopted. Abbreviations for names of journals are in accordance with *The World List of Scientific Periodicals*.

CONTENTS

CHAPTER 1

INTRODUCTION

1.1 *The Problem*

ELEMENTS and chemical compounds may exist, under suitable conditions of temperature and pressure, in three different physical states called, respectively, the solid, liquid and gaseous states. The solid state is stable at low temperatures and/or high pressures; the liquid state is stable in an intermediate range of temperatures and pressures, and the gaseous state is stable at high temperatures and low pressures. The solid state is characterized by high cohesion and rigidity; the liquid state by high cohesion, lack of rigidity and comparatively low resistance to flow; and the gaseous state by low cohesion, lack of rigidity and low resistance to flow. On the molecular level the solid state exhibits a regular crystalline structure and the gaseous state complete molecular disorder, while the liquid state is, in some sense, intermediate between these extremes. These are among the oldest and most basic of scientific facts, yet they still present a considerable challenge. Given a proper understanding it ought to be possible to explain the existence and differences of these three states of matter in terms of their structure and the properties of the units (molecules, atoms, ions) from which they are built. Further, with sufficient knowledge of the properties of the units, it ought to be possible to predict quantitatively in a particular case, the ranges of temperature and pressure in which solid, liquid or gas will exist, and the detailed properties of solid, liquid and gas. This question of prediction, or of partial prediction and correlation, is of fundamental importance to the technologist, for example, to the chemical engineer.

Thus the objectives of a theory concerning the properties of matter are to give a satisfactory description of the structure, to explain how the properties of the molecules, atoms or ions determine the particular structure which is adopted in given conditions, and to provide quantitative correlations between macroscopic properties and the properties of the individual molecules, atoms or ions. To a considerable extent these objectives can be attained for solids and dilute gases, in the first case because of the comparative simplicity of the regular crystalline arrangement, and in the second case because the molecules spend much of their time moving entirely independently of one another. In the case of liquids and highly compressed gases neither of these simplifying features is present, and the theoretical problems are much more difficult, and so far by no means completely solved.

The attempts that have been made to formulate a theory of liquids fall into two broad classes, differing primarily in the emphasis they give to the first two of the three objectives outlined above. Theories of one class start from a description of the structure, usually a simplified and approximate description, leaving the question of how the structure is determined by the molecular properties to be answered after the fact. These theories are called "lattice" theories because the proposed structure often bears some relation to the regular lattice structure of a crystalline solid. Theories of the other class place emphasis initially on the process by which the intermolecular forces determine the structure, in the hope that a correct mathematical description of this process will lead to equations whose solutions describe the actual structure. Theories of this class are called "distribution function" theories because the equations involve distribution functions specifying the probability of finding sets of molecules in particular configurations. Both of these approaches have respectable antecedents. The first develops logically from methods found to be successful in the theory of solids, while the second draws its ideas to some extent from the equally successful kinetic theory of gases. There is no *a priori* reason to suppose that either approach is more correct or more fundamental than the other. They are based on different methods of describing the same situation, and are in a sense complementary. In the long run, of course, one or the other approach may prove to be easier to handle or more useful. Lattice theories are under discussion here, while distribution function theories are treated in another volume in this series.[1]

A lattice theory of the liquid state starts from a description or picture or model of the structure of liquids. It is clear that the word "structure" has different implications for solids on the one hand and for liquids on the other. A solid has a single, static crystal structure which is only slightly blurred by the thermal motions; in a liquid the instantaneous structure changes continually and grossly, because of the random thermal motions of the molecules. In a solid the molecules vibrate about fixed equilibrium lattice sites, and jumps from one lattice site to another (or to an interstitial site) occur very rarely indeed; this is shown by the experimental fact that diffusion in solids is very slow. In liquids there are no fixed lattice sites and diffusion is much more rapid. Nevertheless there is experimental evidence from the scattering of slow neutrons by liquids which suggests that the molecular motions in a liquid may be described at least approximately as vibrations interrupted by occasional jumps. The photographs of computed molecular trajectories published by Wainwright and Alder lend considerable weight to this picture (see chapter 2). Thus it may not be unreasonable to imagine a static average or ideal structure (or structures) and to suppose that the molecules spend much of their time vibrating in regions defined by the structure or structures. If we are concerned with time-averaged equilibrium properties the occasional jumps may be quite unimportant, though they will be all-important for transport properties, such as diffusion. This is the point of view adopted by the lattice theories, which are therefore better fitted to deal with equilibrium properties than with transport properties. In fact we are concerned here primarily with the theory of the equilibrium properties of liquids. The discussion will be confined to molecular liquids, that is liquids composed of chemically saturated, electrically neutral molecules. Metallic liquids, in which the conduction electrons play an important part, and ionic liquids such as fused salts have special properties which would broaden the field of discussion too far. Nevertheless many of the basic ideas should also apply to liquids of these types.

For calculating equilibrium properties the methods of equilibrium statistical mechanics are available. According to classical statistical mechanics the equilibrium properties may be calculated by averaging with an appropriate weighting factor over all accessible spatial configurations of the molecules. The meaning of "accessible" and the nature of the weighting factor depend on the particular conditions— whether for example the system is considered at fixed temperature or at fixed energy. The point to be made here is that in using statistical mechanics we do not have to consider the *dynamics* of the system of molecules at all. Thus from this point of view the distinction between "vibrations" and "jumps" or some more complicated form of motion is meaningless and irrelevant. The purpose of the model or ideal structure in statistical mechanics is simply to provide a convenient *classification* of the actual configurations available to the molecules, in order to make the required averaging possible. In fact starting from a given model or ideal structure, it is usually possible to develop a formal sequence of mathematical approximations, the results of which should ultimately converge to the correct results for the liquid. In practice the detailed evaluation of these approximations rapidly becomes prohibitively difficult, so that to obtain a workable theory it is essential to choose a model or ideal structure which is already as close as possible to the real structure of the liquid. These ideas will be developed more explicitly in later chapters; they are mentioned here to indicate that the tentative way in which we introduce the model or ideal structure does not necessarily imply a lack of rigour or accuracy in the final form of the theory.

The theories to be considered are the "cell" or "free volume" theories, which use as model a regular lattice structure with all lattice sites occupied; the "hole" theories, which use a similar model with some of the lattice sites unoccupied; the "tunnel" theory, based on a partially disordered lattice structure; and the "Monte Carlo" and "molecular dynamics" methods, in which the available volume is divided into large cells containing many molecules and the averaging is performed by direct numerical methods.

A critical discussion of these theories will be given in the following chapters. Anticipating this discussion the following general remarks can be made. The Monte Carlo and molecular dynamics methods undoubtedly lead to correct results provided that the "cells" chosen are sufficiently large. These approaches do not provide a simple description of the nature of the liquid state, and they require a great deal of computation in each individual case. The latter difficulty may be minimized in future by the use of "perturbation" techniques to extend the range of application of the calculated results. The cell and hole theories are not in very good agreement with either the direct structural evidence from X-ray and neutron diffraction or the experimental evidence on thermodynamic properties. Recent work indicates that the cell theory actually describes the *solid* state. Nevertheless the cell theory in the form due to Lennard-Jones and Devonshire (see chapter 4) has been very useful in interpreting the properties of liquids and liquid mixtures. To some extent its success may be due to the fact that the thermodynamic differences between liquid and solid states are comparatively small and can be neglected for some purposes. It remains to be seen whether a development of this approach can lead to a theory sufficiently precise to distinguish between liquid and solid states. The tunnel model has not yet been fully investigated but seems at present to be in reasonable agreement with both structural and thermodynamic evidence for liquids at high densities (i.e. well below the critical temperature). This partially disordered structure may prove to be a better starting point for a theory than the regular structure on which the cell and hole theories are based.

1.2 *The Experimental Evidence*

The experimental evidence concerning the properties of liquids falls into three classes: (i) direct structural evidence from X-ray and neutron diffraction, (ii) thermodynamic evidence from measurement of equilibrium properties, (iii) evidence from measurement of non-equilibrium properties such as viscosity, thermal conductivity and diffusion coefficients.

The information which can be derived from X-ray and neutron diffraction can be summarized in the so-called "radial distribution function", which describes the distribution of molecules around a given central molecule selected for consideration. Results for liquid argon at 84°K are shown in Fig. 1.1; the quantity plotted is the ratio

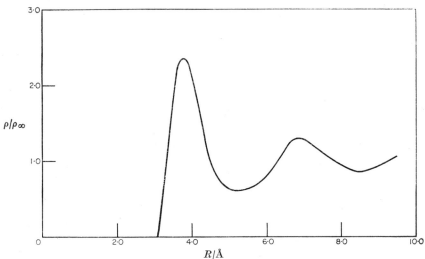

Fig. 1.1. The radial distribution function for argon at 84°K; the density at distance R from a given molecule divided by the mean density. From neutron diffraction data of Henshaw (*Phys. Rev.* **105**, 976, 1957).

of the density at distance R from the central molecule to the average density. Clearly this function contains a good deal of information about the structure, though it does not determine the structure completely. A satisfactory theoretical model should be in agreement with these structural facts.

The thermodynamic information is derived from measurements of density, compressibility, vapour pressures, heats of fusion and vaporization and specific heat. In principle it could be summarized by specifying the free energy of the liquid as a function of temperature and density. Quantities such as compressibility and specific heat could then be derived by differentiating with respect to density and temperature, and the liquid–gas and liquid–solid equilibria could be derived by the thermodynamic procedure of equating chemical potentials. In fact theories are tested by comparing calculated and experimental values of density, compressibility, specific heat, vapour pressure and critical temperature, density and pressure. Of course these comparisons require knowledge of the forces between the molecules in order that the theoretical predictions can be made; this information is derived from the properties of the gaseous and solid states. From a purely qualitative point of view the most striking thermodynamic facts are that the density of the liquid is only slightly lower (in most cases) than that of the solid, while the energy and entropy of the liquid are only a little higher than those of the solid; the difference between liquid and gas is very much greater (at temperatures well below the critical temperature) than the difference between liquid and solid.

The information that can be derived from measurement of transport properties (viscosity, thermal conductivity, diffusion coefficients) in the liquid state is at present purely qualitative because of formidable theoretical difficulties in interpretation. The principal qualitative facts of which a satisfactory theory ought to take note are the relative ease of diffusion and flow in liquids as compared with solids.

1.3 *The Forces between Molecules*

When two molecules approach very closely they repel one another strongly because their electronic atmospheres overlap and the electrostatic repulsion between their positively charged nuclei is no longer completely shielded. At rather larger distances the molecules attract one another by virtue of the "van der Waals" or "dispersion" forces. The simplest way of picturing the origin of these forces is to say that fluctuations in the electronic atmosphere of one molecule produce an instantaneous electrostatic dipole which polarizes the second molecule and attracts the resultant induced dipole. Although the time average of the fluctuating dipole moment is zero (for symmetrical molecules) the average attractive force depends on the average of the square of the dipole moment, which is positive. These attractive forces fall off rapidly with distance and are negligible beyond distances of a few ångstroms. Unsymmetrical molecules may have permanent asymmetries of electric charge distribution, and in this case there will be additional forces which will of course depend on the orientations of the molecules concerned. However, in the simplest case of highly symmetrical molecules, with which we shall be largely concerned, it is a good approximation to say that the force between two molecules (or the potential energy from which the force may be derived by differentiation) depends only on the distance between the centres of the two molecules.

For very simple systems such as two interacting helium atoms the potential energy of interaction can be calculated *a priori* from quantum mechanics. It is found that the potential energy has large positive values for small separations and falls rapidly as the separation increases, passing through a negative minimum and tending to zero as the separation becomes large. Approximate quantal calculations show that the general features of the interaction should be similar for molecules with more electrons. In particular they show that for large separations, the potential energy of interaction should be proportional to the inverse sixth power of the separation. However, quantum mechanics can not at present provide detailed quantitative information on the interaction between many-electron molecules. For this reason it is usual to use a suitable empirical formula for the potential energy as function of distance, the constants in the formula being determined from the properties of the gas and solid. The second virial coefficient and viscosity of the gas, and the density, cohesive energy and specific heat of the solid are the properties most used in this connection. A simple and commonly used empirical potential is the "Lennard-Jones 12–6 potential", described by (1), in which R is the distance between the *centres* of the two molecules:

$$u(R) = 4\epsilon[(\sigma/R)^{12} - (\sigma/R)^{6}] \qquad (1.3.1)$$

This function has the right qualitative features as shown by Fig. 1.2. It contains two disposable constants, an energy ϵ and a length σ. With suitably chosen constants it appears to be capable of giving a reasonably accurate description of the interactions between inert gas atoms and probably of the interactions between comparatively simple molecules such as non-polar diatomic molecules. Tabulated values of the constants ϵ and σ are available for a variety of molecules.[2] For the case of argon, on which many of our comparisons with experiment will be based, we shall adopt the values $\epsilon/k = 119\cdot8°K$, $\sigma = 3\cdot405Å$ derived by Michels *et al.*,[3] from measurements of second virial coefficients. Much of the work in the theory of liquids has been based on the 12–6 function, which will be used extensively in this book. However it must not be concluded that the 12–6 potential gives an *exact* description of the potential for any real system; for example Guggenheim and McGlashan[3] have shown recently that the potential function for interaction of two argon atoms differs appreciably from the 12–6 function, and requires a formula with more than two disposable constants to describe it accurately.

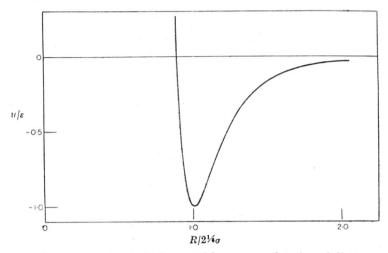

Fɪɢ. 1.2. The 12–6 potential; potential energy as function of distance between the centres of two molecules.

For more complicated but still roughly spherical molecules it may be more accurate to use a function of similar form to (1), but with different exponents n and m instead of 12 and 6 (Lennard-Jones n–m potential). Thus for globular molecules such as SF_6 a 28–7 formula appears to describe the interaction better than the 12–6 formula.[4] For molecules which are highly polar or far from spherical, no potential formula involving only the distance between the molecular centres can be adequate; liquids involving molecules of this kind will be discussed only qualitatively in this book.

In the development of the theory of fluids considerable use has been made of a much simpler molecular model, namely the rigid spherical molecule for which the potential energy of interaction is positively infinite if the separation is less than the molecular diameter, and zero otherwise. Of course no fluid with such molecules exists in nature, but the model is useful for testing theories, particularly since the properties of the rigid-sphere fluid have been evaluated by extensive Monte Carlo calculations. Because there are no attractive forces this model has no liquid phase but it does show the compressed gas–solid phase transition.

Most calculations of the properties of liquids have assumed that the interactions between different pairs of molecules are *additive*, so that the potential energy of an assembly of molecules is the sum of the potential energies of interaction of all the pairs of molecules:

$$U = \sum_{i<j} u(R_{ij}) \tag{1.3.2}$$

where U is the total potential energy and $u(R_{ij})$ is the potential energy of interaction of molecules i and j, depending only on their separation R_{ij}. In view of the origin of the attractive forces this assumption cannot be exactly true for real assemblies of molecules, since the instantaneous force between molecules 1 and 2 must depend on whether or not molecule 2 is also being polarized by other molecules 3, 4, etc. This question of non-additivity of molecular interactions has been studied both experimentally and theoretically but is not yet thoroughly understood. The fact that the 12–6 potential function derived from gas properties of argon also fits the crystal data[5] suggests that non-additivity is not too important. We will use throughout the assumption of additivity implied by (2), which should at least provide a useful first approximation.

1.4 *Statistical Thermodynamics*

The formulae of statistical thermodynamics which will be used can be summarized briefly as follows. If a system has discrete quantum states 1, 2, 3 ... with energies E_1, E_2, E_3 ... then the "partition function" Z is defined as the sum over all states i of the Boltzmann factor $\exp(-E_i/kT)$:

$$Z = \sum_i \exp(-E_i/kT) \tag{1.4.1}$$

In (1) T is the temperature and k Boltzmann's constant. The Helmholtz free energy A is related to the partition function by the equation

$$A = -kT \ln Z \tag{1.4.2}$$

Clearly Z and A are functions of the temperature and of whatever other variables are needed to specify the system (volume V, number of molecules N for an assembly of N molecules in volume V). If the temperature is sufficiently high so that *classical* statistical mechanics can be used, the *sum* in (1) can be replaced by an *integral* over all the co-ordinates and momenta of the system. For a system of N molecules each of mass m in a volume V, the integration over the momenta can be performed immediately, leading to the result:

$$Z = (2\pi m kT/h^2)^{3N/2} Q \tag{1.4.3}$$

in which h is Planck's constant and Q is the classical *configuration integral*, defined by (4):

$$Q(N, V, T) = (1/N \, !) \int \dots \int \exp\left(-U/kT\right) dx_1 \dots dz_N \qquad (1.4.4)$$

Once A is known as a function of N, V and T, all the thermodynamic properties of the system can be derived; the pressure p is $-\partial A/\partial V$, the entropy is $-\partial A/\partial T$ and so on. Thus in using statistical mechanics to evaluate the thermodynamic properties of a system the problem reduces to that of evaluating the partition function Z defined by (1) or the configuration integral Q defined by (4).

The free energy is most conveniently expressed in terms of the "configurational" free energy $A*$ which is defined as $-kT \ln Q$, and which differs from the free energy defined by (2) by an amount which is independent of density, depending on temperature alone. We shall sometimes consider "excess" thermodynamic functions, defined as the excess of the thermodynamic functions over the values they would have if the substance existed in a hypothetical perfect gas state at the same density and temperature. Since the configuration integral for an ideal gas is V^N/N ! the excess Helmholtz free energy A' is given by

$$A' = -kT \ln (N \, ! \, Q/V^N) \qquad (1.4.5)$$

Definitions of excess energy, entropy, heat capacity, etc., may be derived from this equation by differentiation.

If a class of substances has a common potential energy function apart from scale factors of energy and length, then (5) and (1.3.2) can be used to show that the substances obey the principle of corresponding states. If the potential energy function for the ith substance is given by

$$u_i(R) = \epsilon_i u_0(R/\sigma_i) \qquad (1.4.6)$$

where ϵ_i, σ_i are constants characteristic of the substance i and u_0 is the same function for all the substances, then a change of variable in (5) shows that the configurational Helmholtz free energy for substance i is given by

$$A* = N\epsilon_i f \left(V/N\sigma_i^3, \, kT/\epsilon_i\right) \qquad (1.4.7)$$

In (7) f is the same function for all the substances, being determined solely by the function u_0. In deriving (7) the fact that $A*$ is an extensive property, i.e. proportional to N for fixed V/N, has also been used. Since all configurational thermodynamic properties can be derived from (7) by differentiation it follows that the substances of the class have identical configurational thermodynamic functions provided that energies, volumes, temperatures and pressures are measured in units of ϵ_i, σ_i^3, ϵ_i/k and ϵ_i/σ_i^3, respectively. This is the principle of corresponding states; the more usual statement in terms of critical temperature, pressure and volume follows, if it is recognized that these must be proportional to ϵ_i/k, ϵ_i/σ_i^3 and σ_i^3, respectively. Apart from its practical usefulness this principle simplifies the comparison of theories of liquids with experiments, because a theory which is valid for one substance of the class must be valid for all.

For solids at sufficiently low temperatures the vibrations of the crystal lattice may be treated as harmonic, and the energy levels E_i can be determined in terms of the frequencies of the independent normal lattice vibrations, so that the partition function Z can be evaluated. This procedure is used in the Born–Kármán theory of solids. There are two simplified models which are used in the theory of solids, namely the Debye model which is approximately valid at low temperatures and which replaces the true vibrational spectrum of the lattice by the spectrum of a *continuum*, and the Einstein model which is approximately valid at high temperatures and which replaces the vibrational spectrum by a single frequency corresponding to a single atom vibrating with its neighbours fixed. The Einstein model is seriously wrong at low temperatures because it ignores the existence of low-frequency vibrations in which neighbouring atoms move almost in unison. That is the Einstein model assumes that the motions of different atoms are independent, so that *correlations* between motions of neighbouring atoms are neglected. We shall see later that the Einstein model corresponds closely to the cell theory of liquids in the form due to Lennard-Jones and Devonshire, with the difference that the latter theory does not assume that the vibrations are harmonic.

For gases the configuration integral Q can be evaluated by a "cluster expansion" technique. If the potential energy U is given by (1.3.2) the exponential $\exp\left(-U/kT\right)$ can be written in the form of a product:

$$\exp\left(-U/kT\right) = \prod_{i>j} (1 + f_{ij}) \tag{1.4.8}$$

$$f_{ij} = \exp\left[-u(R_{ij})/kT\right] - 1 \tag{1.4.9}$$

If the product in (8) is expanded one obtains a term with no f_{ij} factor, then a number of terms with one such factor, then a number with two, and so on. In this way the configuration integral can be expressed as a sum of products of "cluster integrals" of which the first few involve integration over the coordinates of only a few molecules. This sum can be transformed to give an expression for the pressure as a power series in the density. The coefficients in this series ("virial coefficients") are "irreducible cluster integrals" which involve integrals of products of f_{ij} factors over the coordinates of relatively few molecules (2 for the second virial coefficient, 3 for the third and so on). The second and third virial coefficients have been evaluated for several potential energy functions, including the 12–6 potential;[2] comparison of experimental and theoretical second virial coefficients is a common way of determining the constants ϵ and σ in the 12–6 formula, (1.3.1). Fourth virial coefficients have so far been evaluated for rigid-sphere and certain square-well potentials,[6] and approximately at high temperatures for the 12–6 potential.[7] The fifth virial coefficient is known approximately for the hard-sphere potential[2] but for no other, and no higher virial coefficients are known for any potential.

The virial series, with neglect of all virial coefficients beyond the fourth or fifth, gives reasonable results for the thermodynamic properties of gases at densities below the critical density. At liquid densities the virial series cannot be used to give useful results. There is a possibility that some kind of analytic continuation might be used to derive results valid in the liquid region from the cluster integral expansion; however, this lies within the province of the distribution function theories and will not be discussed here.

It appears from this brief discussion that the partition function or configuration integral can only be evaluated explicitly when the system under consideration can be broken down into units which are in some sense independent, or almost so. In the theory of solids the independent units are the normal lattice vibrations; in the theory of gases they are the actual molecules. Thus from one point of view the basic problem in the theory of liquids is to find a way of dividing the liquid into a set of independent or almost independent systems. In cell and hole theories a model like the Einstein model is adopted, so that the independent units are molecules vibrating under the influence of fixed neighbours.

There is one exception to the rule that the configuration integral can be evaluated explicitly only for systems of independent or almost independent units, namely the one-dimensional case. The classical configuration integral can be evaluated exactly for a system of molecules constrained to move on a line. This fact is exploited by the tunnel theory, in which the basic units are whole lines of molecules moving in tunnels.

REFERENCES

1. RUSHBROOKE, G. S., *Distribution Function Theories of Fluids*, to be published by Pergamon.
2. HIRSCHFELDER, J. O., CURTISS, C. F. and BIRD, R. B., *Molecular Theory of Gases and Liquids*, Chapman & Hall, London, 1954, p. 157 *et seq.*
3. GUGGENHEIM, E. A. and McGLASHAN, M. L., *Proc. roy. Soc.* 1960, A255, 456; GUGGENHEIM, E. A., *Elements of the Kinetic Theory of Gases*, Pergamon, Oxford, 1960, ch. 15.
4. HAMANN, S. D. and LAMBERT, J. A., *Australian J. Chem.* 1954, 7, 1.
5. DOBBS, E. R. and JONES, G. O., *Rep. Prog. Phys.*, 1957, 20, 516.
6. KATSURA, S., *Phys. Rev.* 1959, 115, 1417.
7. BOYS, S. F. and SHAVITT, I., *Proc. roy. Soc.* 1960, A254, 487.
8. MICHELS, A., WIJKER, HUB. and WIJKER, HK., *Physica* 1949, 15, 627.

CHAPTER 2

MONTE CARLO AND RELATED METHODS

2.1 *Principles*

The molecules in a fluid decide the structure they will adopt by trying all possibilities. Given sufficient computing facilities there is no reason why we should not make a direct mathematical simulation of this process, considering of course a limited number of molecules. With modern developments in electronic computing this has become quite feasible and useful results have been obtained in this way by Metropolis *et al.*,[1,2] by Wood *et al.*[3-6] and by Wainwright and Alder.[7-10]

There are several possible methods. We could select arbitrary initial positions and velocities for the molecules and follow the evolution in time by solving the equations of motion; equilibrium properties would then be determined by time averaging. This is the method of molecular dynamics. Another possibility is to select at random a large number of spatial configurations and average the properties in which we are interested over these configurations, weighting each configuration with the appropriate Boltzmann factor. This method is not feasible because the number of configurations required for satisfactory averaging is enormous. However, a related procedure is to select configurations with frequency proportional to exp $(-U/kT)$, and average over the selected configurations with equal weights. This is the Monte Carlo method. The method of molecular dynamics uses time averaging following the trajectories of the system while the Monte Carlo method uses ensemble averaging. Statistical mechanics assures us that the two methods of averaging should give identical results for equilibrium properties. In fact both methods have been used for systems composed of rigid spherical molecules and the results agree satisfactorily.

The method of molecular dynamics is capable of dealing not only with equilibrium phenomena but also with relaxation and non-equilibrium phenomena. The Monte Carlo method is restricted to equilibrium phenomena but in this field is probably more satisfactory, because the information on molecular velocities provided by the method of molecular dynamics is in a sense redundant in equilibrium situations.

Both methods are restricted by the fact that only a limited number, N, of molecules can be considered; this limitation is imposed by computing speed rather than by information storage requirements. To minimize the effects of this restriction ("surface" effects) a periodic boundary condition is used. It is supposed that the whole of space is filled by repetitions of a fundamental cell of volume V containing N molecules. As a consequence of this the Monte Carlo and molecular dynamics methods are closely related to the simpler cell theories. The fundamental difference is that the cell is large and contains many molecules. Further differences lie in the treatment of the "surface" effects, which are of course much less important with a large cell, and in the fact that other cell theories permit approximate evaluation of the partition function. In the present state of the art of computing, the partition function, and therefore the entropy, cannot be evaluated by these direct numerical methods.

2.2 The Monte Carlo Method

If in a dense system of molecules we select configurations at random a large majority of the selected configurations will have very small values of exp $(-U/kT)$. For example in the rigid sphere system it is overwhelmingly likely that at least two spheres will overlap in a randomly chosen configuration. Thus to obtain satisfactory averages in this way it would be necessary to examine an enormous number of configurations (this is essentially why the partition function itself cannot be evaluated by the Monte Carlo method). For this reason it is more satisfactory to select configurations with frequency proportional to exp $(-U/kT)$. A way of doing this was devised by Metropolis et al.[1] It involves generating a chain of configurations by starting from an arbitrary initial configuration and moving the molecules one at a time according to certain rules.[3]

Suppose that the configuration numbered n in the chain is a certain configuration j with energy U_j. The next configuration, numbered $n + 1$, is to be chosen as follows. Select one of the molecules at random (by the use of random numbers) and consider the configuration l derived from j by moving this molecule from its position with coordinates (x, y, z) to a new position $(x + u, y + v, z + w)$ where u, v and w are three numbers each randomly chosen in the interval $(-\delta, \delta)$. Compute the energy U_l of configuration l. If U_l is less than U_j the next configuration is l. If U_l is greater than U_j, compute exp $[-(U_l - U_j)/kT]$ and compare it with a number randomly chosen in the interval $(0, 1)$.

If the exponential is the smaller, the next configuration is j; if the larger, the next configuration is l. The effect of this is that if U_l is less than U_j the next configuration is l, while if U_l is greater than U_j it is either l or j with respective probabilities $\exp\left[-(U_l - U_j)/kT\right]$ and $\{1 - \exp\left[-(U_l - U_j)/kT\right]\}$. In the case of rigid spherical molecules this rule is very simple: the next configuration is l if the moved molecule does not overlap another molecule, and j if it does. In earlier calculations the molecules were actually moved in ordered rather than random sequence.

It can be proved from the theory of Markov processes that if such a chain is made sufficiently long the frequencies of occurrence of the different configurations j in the chain becomes proportional to $\exp\left(-U_j/kT\right)$. We shall give an outline of this proof. The rules for generating the chain amount to a specification of the conditional probability p_{jl} that if the configuration n in the chain is j, then the configuration $n+1$ will be l. The conditional probability $p_{jl}^{(m)}$ that if configuration n in the chain is j, configuration $n + m$ will be l can be derived from p_{jl} by repeated use of the equations

$$p_{jl}^{(1)} = p_{jl} \tag{2.2.1}$$

$$p_{jl}^{(m)} = \sum_{k'} p_{jk'}^{(m-1)} p_{k'l} \tag{2.2.2}$$

We are interested in the limiting behaviour of $p_{jl}^{(m)}$ as m becomes very large. It is known from the theory of Markov processes[11] that, provided certain conditions of accessibility of configurations are satisfied, then the $p_{jl}^{(m)}$ tend as m tends to infinity to unique limits w_l which are independent of j; further these limits w_l are determined by (3), (4) and (5).

$$w_l > 0 \tag{2.2.3}$$

$$\sum_l w_l = 1 \tag{2.2.4}$$

$$w_l = \sum_j p_{jl} w_l \tag{2.2.5}$$

The conditions of accessibility require that it should be possible using the rules for generating the chain to pass from any configuration j to any other configuration k in a finite number of steps. We wish to show that the rules for generating the chain imply that w_l is equal to $c \exp\left(-U_l/kT\right)$ where c is a normalizing constant.

If $x_j^{(\alpha, r)}$ denotes the αth ($\alpha = 1, 2, 3$) Cartesian coordinate of molecule

r in configuration j then the values of p_{jl} corresponding to the rules set out above may be specified thus:

$$p_{jl} = A_{jl}, \qquad l \neq j, \quad U_l \leqslant U_j \qquad\qquad (2.2.6)$$

$$p_{jl} = A_{jl} \exp\left[-(U_l - U_j)/kT\right], \qquad l \neq j, \quad U_l > U_j \qquad (2.2.7)$$

$$p_{jj} = 1 - \sum_{l \neq j} p_{jl} \qquad\qquad (2.2.8)$$

where A_{jl} is $1/(8N\delta^3)$ if for $r = 1, 2 \dots N$ and $r' = 1, 2 \dots N$ and $\alpha = 1, 2, 3$ we have

$$x_j^{(\alpha, r)} = x_l^{(\alpha, r)}, \, r \neq r' \qquad\qquad (2.2.9)$$

$$\left| x_j^{(\alpha, r')} - x_l^{(\alpha, r')} \right| < \delta \qquad\qquad (2.2.10)$$

and A_{jl} is zero otherwise.

With these values of p_{jl} and with w_l equal to $c \exp(-U_l/kT)$ it is easily verified that the "principle of microscopic reversibility" holds in the form

$$w_j \, p_{jl} = w_l \, p_{lj} \qquad\qquad (2.2.11)$$

If in addition c is chosen so that (4) is satisfied then substitution of (11) shows that (5) is satisfied identically. Thus with p_{jl} defined by (6)–(10) we have proved that

$$\begin{aligned} w_l &= \lim_{m \to \infty} p_{jl}^{(m)} \\ &= c \exp(-U_l/kT) \end{aligned} \qquad\qquad (2.2.12)$$

This means that *whatever the starting configuration* the frequencies of occurrence of configuration l in a long chain become proportional to $\exp(-U_l/kT)$. Thus if a configurational property is averaged over all configurations of a long chain the resulting average converges to the ensemble average corresponding to the temperature T. It is usual to start the molecules from a regular lattice configuration and to omit the early configurations from the averages, since these would show the effects of the initial configuration and slow the convergence. For molecules interacting according to the 12–6 potential an IBM 704 calculator generated about 19000 configurations per hour for a system of 32 molecules and 6500 configurations per hour for 108 molecules. Since the number of configurations required for satisfactory averaging is 50000 or more the amount of computing involved is formidable.

Difficulties arise if the configurations fall into classes such that the probabilities for transitions between classes are very low; for example these classes might be ordered, solid-like configurations on one hand and disordered, fluid-like configurations on the other. In such cases the chain tends to include long sequences of configurations from one class, with jumps from class to class happening only rarely. In fact in the original calculations on the rigid-sphere system[2] the apparent solid–fluid transition was overlooked because the chains were not sufficiently long. In general it is difficult to obtain satisfactory averages in the neighbourhood of phase transitions. It remains to be seen how serious these problems are for liquids—the calculations using the 12–6 potential were performed for a temperature above the critical temperature.

We have mentioned that in order to reduce the importance of "surface" effects the whole of space is supposed to be filled with periodic repetitions ("images") of the fundamental cell, each containing N molecules in the same relative positions. The question then arises which interactions shall be included in computing the potential energy U as a sum of pair interactions. In most of the calculations the "minimum image distance" rule has been used. According to this rule the energy sum contains one term for each pair of molecules in the fundamental cell [i.e. $N(N-1)/2$ terms in all] but for each pair the interaction distance is taken as the shortest distance between any two images of the two molecules. Thus if an image B' of a molecule B is closer to another molecule A than B itself then the distance between A and B' is used in computing the energy. This is satisfactory for rigid spherical molecules, but leads to errors for a potential of longer range such as the 12–6 potential. In fact it includes correctly all interactions at distances smaller than half the edge of the fundamental cell but omits an increasing fraction of interactions as the distance increases until finally for distances greater than the cell diagonal no interactions are included. If the number of molecules is small these omissions may lead to serious error. A more satisfactory alternative is to include all interactions of molecules in the basic cell with all molecules and images within a certain maximum distance, but this takes more calculating time. In fact, provided that suitable corrections for longer-range interactions are applied to the results obtained with the "minimum image distance" rule, they agree satisfactorily with the results obtained by the latter method.

The radial distribution function can be determined by counting for each configuration the number of intermolecular distances lying within specified ranges, and averaging the resulting numbers over all configurations. The pressure may be determined by calculating the average of the "virial of intermolecular forces" W, defined by

$$W = - \sum_{i \neq j} R_{ij} \, \partial u(R_{ij}) / \partial R_{ij} \qquad (2.2.13)$$

The pressure is given in terms of the average value $\overline{W}$ of W by the relation[12]

$$pV = NkT + \tfrac{1}{3} \overline{W} \qquad (2.2.14)$$

For the particular case of rigid spherical molecules the pressure can be derived from the radial distribution function according to the equation[2]

$$pV = NkT \left[1 + \frac{2\pi}{3} D^3 n(D) \right] \qquad (2.2.15)$$

where D is the rigid sphere diameter and $n(D)$ is the density of neighbours at distance D from a central molecule (extrapolated from larger distances).

The molar configurational energy and heat capacity E^* and C_v^* can be determined from the averages $\overline{U}$ and $\overline{U^2}$ of U and U^2 by the relations

$$E^*/RT = \overline{U}/NkT \qquad (2.2.16)$$

$$C_v^* = N \, [\overline{U^2} - (\overline{U})^2]/(NkT)^2 \qquad (2.2.17)$$

2.3   The Method of Molecular Dynamics[7–10]

In this method the equations of motion are solved by a step-wise procedure. So far calculations have been made only for rigid-sphere and square-well potentials. With these potentials the molecular velocities are changed only by binary collisions. The periodic boundary condition is used, so that a molecule leaving the fundamental cell through one face re-enters it through the opposite face; in this way the number of molecules in the cell remain constant. In determining when and where the next collision will occur a convention analogous to the "minimum image distance" rule is adopted. The molecules are started in a regular array with equal speeds but random directions of motion. The velocity distribution tends rapidly to the Maxwell distribution. The total energy of course remains constant and determines the temperature.

For a system of 100 molecules an IBM 704 computer calculates about 2000 collisions (or 40 collisions per molecule) per hour of machine time. The number of collisions per molecule per hour of machine time

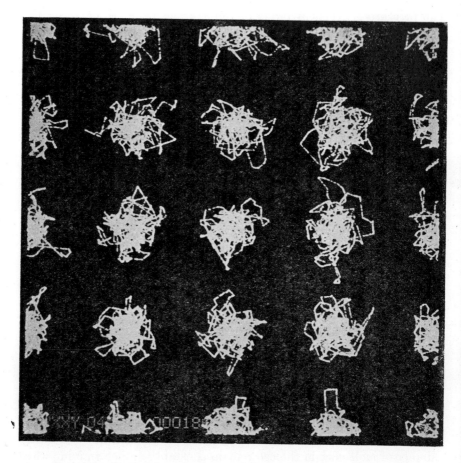

FIG. 2.1. Projected molecular trajectories for rigid spheres with $V/V_0 = 1.525$; 32 particles in a cubic box performing 3000 collisions in the solid region. After Wainwright and Alder.[9] (Reproduced with permission from *Il Nuovo Cimento*).

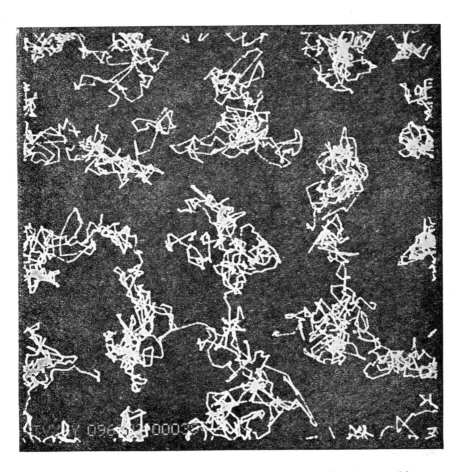

FIG. 2.2. Projected molecular trajectories for rigid spheres with $V/V_0 = 1.525$; 32 particles in a cubic box performing 3000 collisions in the fluid region. After Wainwright and Alder.[9] (Reproduced with permission from *Il Nuovo Cimento*).

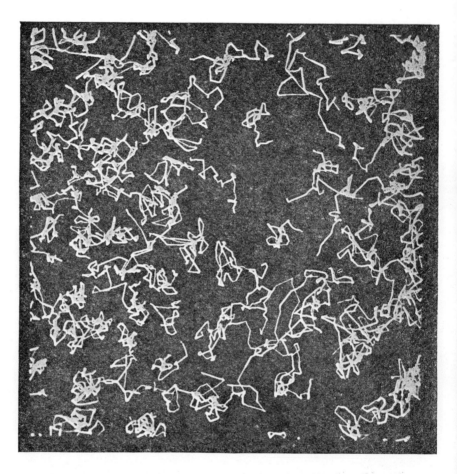

Fig. 2.3. Projected molecular trajectories for 108 molecules with square-well attractive field in the liquid–vapour region, performing about 3000 collisions. After Alder and Wainwright.[8] (Reproduced with permission from *Il Nuovo Cimento*).

is roughly inversely proportional to the square of the number of molecules. In the actual calculations it is convenient to record the detailed information on molecular positions and velocities on magnetic tape for later analysis. From this information it is possible to derive the velocity distribution (of interest in non-equilibrium situations), the pair and triplet spatial distribution functions, the pressure and collision rate and the average potential energy. It is also possible to display the information on a cathode-ray picture tube, thus obtaining a graphic representation of the molecular motions. Figs. 2.1, 2.2 and 2.3 show results obtained in this way. The white lines are projections of the trajectories of molecules in the fundamental cell onto a face of the cell. The difference between solid and fluid states is striking. It is also of great interest that even in the fluid state the molecules appear to vibrate for considerable periods in localized regions.

2.4 *Results*

Extensive calculations have been made using both Monte Carlo and molecular dynamic methods for rigid spherical molecules in two and three dimensions. The results obtained by the two methods are now in agreement[4-10], although the earliest Monte Carlo calculations[1,2] gave incorrect results at low densities because the chains of configurations were not sufficiently long to detect the transition to disordered states.

For both two-dimensional and three-dimensional systems the following behaviour is observed. If the molecules are started in a regular lattice arrangement and the density is high then the molecules remain in configurations very close to this regular arrangement (cf. Fig. 2.1). If, however, the density is lower the system after some time makes an abrupt transition to a relatively disordered arrangement (cf. Fig. 2.2), and at the same time the pressure rises. At low densities the system will remain in this disordered state, but there is an intermediate range of densities in which the system may make occasional transitions between ordered and disordered states. By starting the molecules in specially chosen disordered configurations it is possible to extend the disordered state to higher densities.

The ordered state, which gives lower values of the pressure, is regarded as a *solid* state, while the disordered, high pressure state is identified with the fluid state. This identification is made convincing by the results for 12–6 molecules discussed below and by the nature of the molecular trajectories shown in Figs. 2.1–2.3.

The calculated pressures for two- and three-dimensional systems are

c

shown in Figs. 2.4 and 2.5. In each case the isotherm has two branches corresponding to solid and fluid states. For comparison pressures calculated from the cell theory of Wood[13] and from the virial series with sixth and higher virial coefficients omitted are also shown. For both two- and three-dimensional systems the pressures calculated from the cell theory lie below the "solid" branch of the isotherm but appear

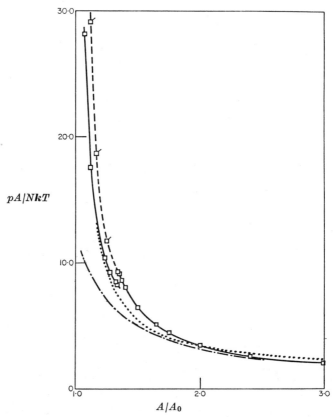

Fig. 2.4. Pressure–area isotherm for rigid spheres in two dimensions. Monte Carlo results for 48 particles started in regular hexagonal arrangement shown thus □ and for 48 molecules started in a special disorded arrangment shown thus ⧄. Free volume theory thus · · · · · · and virial series including fifth coefficient thus — · — · —. (Reproduced with permission from *J. Chem. Phys.*).

to approach it at high densities. The pressures calculated from the virial series lie below the "fluid" branch, corresponding to the fact that higher virial coefficients which are positive have been omitted. The fact that the virial series gives pressures very close to the "solid" branch of the isotherm in the three-dimensional case is almost certainly a coincidence.

The Monte Carlo method has also been used[3] for molecules interacting according to the 12–6 potential. The only detailed results so far published refer to a temperature which is about twice the critical temperature, so that there is no liquid phase. However, the transition between compressed gas and solid is clearly shown. The calculated compression

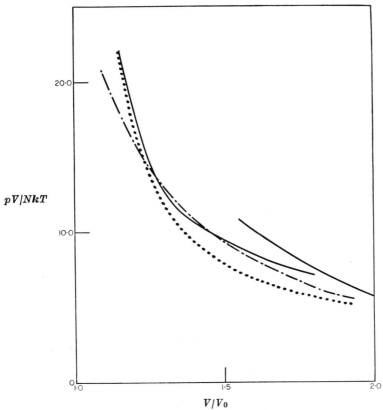

pV/NkT

V/V_0

FIG. 2.5. Pressure–volume isotherm for rigid spheres in three dimensions. Molecular dynamics results shown thus ————, free volume theory thus $\cdots\cdots$ and virial series including fifth coefficient thus — · — · —. Reproduced with permission from *J. Chem. Phys.*).

ratios and configurational energies are shown in Figs. 2.6 and 2.7 Also shown are values calculated from the cell theory of Lennard-Jones and Devonshire (see chapter 4) and experimental data for argon at 55°C (this temperature corresponds to $kT/\epsilon = 2\cdot74$).

There is a transition in the region $V/V_0 = 0\cdot90$–$0\cdot95$ which can only be the compressed gas–solid transition. This is shown by Fig. 2.6, and even more clearly by Fig. 2.7. The theory of Lennard-Jones and Devonshire agrees with the Monte Carlo results on the high-density (solid) side of this transition but not on the gas side. The Monte Carlo compression ratios and energies agree well with Michels' measurements on argon at comparatively low pressures, but not so well with Bridgman's measurements at high pressures. There is evidence[3] that Bridgman's measured pressures may be too high, so that this disagreement is probably not serious. The pressure at the melting transition indicated by the Monte Carlo method corresponds to a value of about 10000 atm for argon at 55°C; extrapolation of the data of Robinson[14]

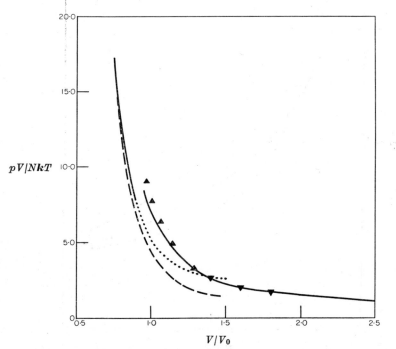

FIG. 2.6. Pressure–volume isotherm for 12–6 fluid with $kT/\epsilon = 2.74$. Monte Carlo results shown thus ————, cell theory of Lennard-Jones and Devonshire (chapter 4) thus ······, cell theory of Dahler and Hirschfelder (chapter 5) thus — — — —. Experimental data of Michels thus ▼ and Bridgman thus ▲. (Reproduced with permission from *J. Chem. Phys.*).

using the empirical relation of Simon[3] suggests an experimental value of about 13500 atm. This difference, if it is real, could be due to the small number of molecules used in the calculations (32 in most of the work) or to inadequacy of the 12–6 potential in the repulsive region for argon or to deviations from additivity of potential energies in argon.

Both the Monte Carlo method and the method of molecular dynamics can clearly give good results for the properties of compressed gases (at densities even higher than ordinary liquid densities) and of solids. There is little published information on the use of these methods for liquids as such. Wood has pointed out[15] that a difficulty arises from the fact that the pressure must be calculated as a small difference of two large quantities which cannot be calculated with high accuracy. It is impossible to say at present how serious this difficulty will prove to be.

The methods are at their best in calculating properties which depend only on the pair distribution function, such as pressure and energy. The convergence of the averaging procedures is less satisfactory for

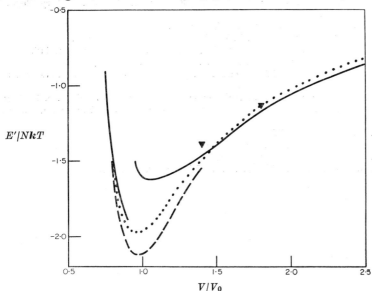

FIG. 2.7. Excess energy–volume isotherm for 12–6 fluid with $kT/\epsilon = 2.74$. Monte Carlo results shown thus ————, cell theory of Lennard-Jones and Devonshire (chapter 4) thus ·······, cell theory of Dahler and Hirschfelder (chapter 5) thus ————. Experimental data of Michels thus ▼. (Reproduced with permission from *J. Chem. Phys.*).

the heat capacity, which depends on the triplet distribution function, and neither method can estimate the entropy which cannot be expressed in terms of distribution functions of low order.

The disadvantage common to both the Monte Carlo method and the method of molecular dynamics (apart from the lack of a simple picture or description of the structure) is the amount of computation required to obtain results. This will become less important as computing methods develop. It can be circumvented to some extent by using perturbation methods to derive results for slightly different potential energy functions from computed results for a given function. Work along these lines has been described by Smith and Alder.[16] It is also probably true that *any* theory of the liquid state with claims to accuracy will involve heavy computations.

REFERENCES

1. METROPOLIS, N. *et al.*, *J. chem. Phys.* 1953, **21**, 1087.
2. ROSENBLUTH, M. N. and ROSENBLUTH, A. W., *J. chem. Phys.* 1954, **22**, 881.
3. WOOD, W. W. and PARKER, F. R., *J. chem. Phys.* 1957, **27**, 720.
4. WOOD, W. W. and JACOBSON, J. D., *J. chem. Phys.* 1957, **27**, 1207.
5. WOOD, W. W., PARKER, F. R. and JACOBSON, J. D., *Nuovo Cim.* 1958, **9**, Suppl. 1, 133.
6. JACOBSON, J. D. and WOOD, W. W., Los Alamos Scientific Laboratory Report, No. GMX–10–37, 1959.
7. ALDER, B. J. and WAINWRIGHT, T. W., *J. chem. Phys.* 1957, **27**, 1208.
8. ALDER, B. J. and WAINWRIGHT, T. W., *J. chem. Phys.* 1959, **31**, 459.
9. WAINWRIGHT, T. W. and ALDER, B. J., *Nuovo Cim.* 1958, **9**, Suppl. 1, 116.
10. ALDER, B. J. and WAINWRIGHT, T. W., *J. chem. Phys.* 1960, **33**, 1439.
11. FELLER, W., *Probability Theory and Its Applications*, Wiley, New York, ch. 15, 1950.
12. TER HAAR, D., *Elements of Statistical Mechanics*, Reinhardt, New York, p. 10, 1954; GUGGENHEIM, E. A., *Elements of the Kinetic Theory of Gases*, Pergamon, Oxford, p. 74, 1960.
13. WOOD, W. W., *J. chem. Phys.* 1952, **20**, 1334.
14. ROBINSON, D. W., *Proc. roy. Soc.* 1954, **A225**, 393.
15. WOOD, W. W., Personal communication.
16. SMITH, E. B. and ALDER, B. J., *J. chem. Phys.* 1959, **30**, 1191.

CHAPTER 3

SIMPLE LATTICE THEORIES

3.1 *Lattice Models*

The purpose of this chapter is to introduce the models and assumptions on which lattice theories are based in terms uncomplicated by mathe-matical detail. To this end we shall describe the simplest possible form of cell theory, hole theory and tunnel theory, as well as the order–disorder theory of melting. The refinements of these simple ideas that are required to develop satisfactory and convincing theories will become evident in later chapters.

3.2 *A Simple Cell Theory*[1]

The cell model is based on the idea that each molecule in a liquid or compressed gas spends much of its time confined by its neighbours to a comparatively restricted region. We picture the neighbouring molecules as forming a "cage" or "cell" in which the central molecule moves. From this point of view the local molecular environment in a liquid is not very different from that in a solid, although there is no long-range order.

The simplest possible assumption is that the molecules move entirely independently of one another in their cells. To make this definite we suppose that in considering the motion of a central molecule we can imagine the neighbours which form the cage as fixed at the centres of their respective cells. There is of course a contradiction in this because at the same time these neighbouring molecules move in *their* cages. The error is precisely that of the Einstein model; we are neglecting correlations between the motions of neighbouring molecules.

We shall further suppose that all the cages are identical, and that each contains just one molecule. The latter assumption means that the model imposes severe restrictions on fluctuations of density, and does not permit the molecules to share the volume fully. More precisely it restricts the configuration space available to the molecules to that fraction of the total configuration space in which every cell contains one molecule. At low densities this has the consequence that the calculated entropy is too low. The additional entropy that would arise if the molecules were given access to the whole configuration space is called the "communal entropy", since it arises from sharing the volume.

For rigid spherical molecules the value of the configuration integral corresponding to these assumptions is given simply by (1):

$$Q(N, V, T) = (1/N\ !) \sum{}^* v_\mathrm{f}^N \qquad (3.2.1)$$

In (1) the summation $\sum{}^*$ is to be taken over all arrangements of the N molecules in the N cells, with the restriction that each cell contains only one molecule. The "free volume" v_f is the volume available to the centre of a molecule in its cage (calculated on the assumption that the neighbours remain fixed at the centres of their cells). Of course the free volume v_f is much less than the total volume V, and at high densities it is also much less than V/N. Since there are $N\ !$ different arrangements of N molecules in N cells (if each cell contains one molecule), (1) gives

$$Q(N, V, T) = v_\mathrm{f}^N \qquad (3.2.2)$$

If the restriction that each cell contains one molecule were not imposed there would be N^N arrangements of N molecules in N cells. For large values of N the ratio of N^N to $N\ !$ is e^N; this factor is the source of the "communal entropy". In an attempt to allow for the communal entropy the configuration integral (2) is sometimes multiplied by e^N. This is unjustifiable because at high densities arrangements in which more than one molecule occupy a single cell must give very small contributions to the configuration integral (cf. chapter 6).

To evaluate the free volume it is necessary to make further assumptions about the arrangement of the neighbouring molecules. If the nearest neighbours lie on a sphere of radius a about the cell centre then a good approximation to the free volume should be the volume of a sphere of radius $(a - D)$, since the central molecule can certainly move the distance $(a - D)$ from its cell centre before colliding with another molecule. This leads to the result

$$v_\mathrm{f} = (4\pi/3)\ (a - D)^3 \qquad (3.2.3)$$

This result underestimates the free volume because $(a - D)$ is actually the *minimum* distance the central molecule can move from its cell centre to collision; in most directions it can move further. The value given by (3) would be correct if the neighbours were "smeared" uniformly over the sphere of radius a. This "smearing" approximation is discussed further in chapter 6.

The result (3) is still not explicit because the average nearest-neighbour distance a is not known in terms of the volume per molecule V/N. To determine the relation between these quantities it is necessary to make a further assumption about the structure. If it is assumed that the cell centres lie on a regular lattice then it follows that

$$a^3 = \gamma'(V/N) \qquad (3.2.4)$$

where the constant γ' depends on the particular lattice considered. For cubic close-packed (face-centred cubic) and hexagonal close-packed lattices γ' is $\sqrt{2}$, for the body-centred cubic and simple cubic lattices it is $3\sqrt{(3)}/4$ and 1 respectively. The smallest possible volume V_0' for a given lattice structure, i.e. the volume when nearest neighbours are in contact, is given by

$$D^3 = \gamma'(V_0'/N) \qquad (3.2.5)$$

Using (4) and (5), equation (3) becomes

$$v_f = (4\pi\gamma'/3N)[V^{1/3} - (V_0')^{1/3}]^3 \qquad (3.2.6)$$

It is a reasonable presumption that the system would choose the lattice structure leading to the lowest free energy, which means here the largest free volume or the largest value of γ'. Thus either the face-centred cubic or hexagonal close-packed structure is indicated. However, for the moment we shall not specify a particular lattice structure.

The assumption that the cell centres form a regular lattice is always made in cell and hole theories, because no satisfactory alternative is known. It is possible that the work of Bernal[2] on irregular ideal structures may lead to a better assumption, but there are grave theoretical difficulties involved. The regular lattice of cell centres brings back the very feature of long-range order which we wished to avoid. It means that the only molecular configurations being considered are those which are in some sense close to a regular lattice configuration. But the Monte Carlo and molecular dynamics calculations (chapter 2) indicate that regular solid-like structures on one hand and irregular fluid-like structures on the other involve different and apparently somewhat separated regions of configuration space. Thus it should not be surprising if the cell theory actually describes solids rather than fluids.

Using (6) for the free volume the configurational Helmholtz free energy is found to be

$$A^* = - NkT \ln v_f$$

$$= NkT \ln \left(\frac{3N}{4\pi\gamma'}\right) - 3NkT \ln [V^{1/3} - (V_0')^{1/3}] \qquad (3.2.7)$$

The configurational entropy is

$$S^* = - \partial A^*/\partial T$$

$$= - Nk \ln \left(\frac{3N}{4\pi\gamma'}\right) + 3Nk \ln [V^{1/3} - (V_0')^{1/3}] \qquad (3.2.8)$$

and the pressure is

$$p = - \partial A^*/\partial V$$

$$= (NkT/V)/[1 - (V_0'/V)^{1/3}] \qquad (3.2.9)$$

The pressure–volume isotherm (9) depends on the particular lattice structure only through the value of V_0'. If we now assume that the lattice is either face-centred cubic or hexagonal close-packed we find

$$p = (NkT/V)/[1 - (V_0/V)^{1/3}] \qquad (3.2.10)$$

where V_0 is $ND^3/\sqrt{2}$. The values of the pressure calculated from (10) are identical with the "free volume" values plotted in Fig. 2.5, although the latter results were actually derived from a more complicated theory (see chapter 5).

The simple cell theory described here does not predict the transition from solid to fluid behaviour which the accurate Monte Carlo and molecular dynamics results show to exist for rigid spherical molecules. The cell theory isotherm is in good agreement with the *solid* branch of the isotherm at high densities. At lower densities the agreement is not so good; it is to be expected that the effects of the "smearing" approximation and of the complete neglect of the "communal entropy" and correlation effects will be more important at lower densities. The cell theory isotherm does not agree well with the fluid branch of the isotherm. We shall find that this behaviour is characteristic of cell theories.

For more complicated systems with attractive forces between the molecules the assumption that the molecules move independently in their cells implies that the potential energy is approximated by the expression

$$U = U_0 + \sum_{i} [\psi(\mathbf{r}_i) - \psi(0)] \qquad (3.2.11)$$

where U_0 is the energy when all the molecules are at the centres of their cells and $[\psi(\mathbf{r}_i) - \psi(0)]$ is the change of potential energy when the molecule i is displaced from the centre of its cell by the vector $\mathbf{r}_i$, with the other molecules remaining at the centres of their cells. We can define a "free volume" in this case by the equation

$$v_f = \int \exp\{ - [\psi(\mathbf{r}_i)] - \psi(0)]/kT\} \, d\mathbf{r}_i \qquad (3.2.12)$$

The free volume defined in this way depends on the attractive forces as well as the repulsive forces; it is a function of temperature as well as density. The configuration integral is given by

$$Q = v_f^N \exp\left(-U_0/kT\right) \qquad (3.2.13)$$

Development of these ideas leads to the theory of Lennard-Jones and Devonshire (chapter 4).

A simpler approach, developed by Eyring and Hirschfelder[3,4] is based on combining the expression (8) for the configurational entropy with an empirical expression for the configurational energy. This uses the idea that the free volume and entropy are determined primarily by the repulsive forces and the energy primarily by the attractive forces. Strictly speaking such a separation of effects cannot be rigorously justified, but it leads to a useful semiempirical equation. It is found that the molar configurational energy for many substances can be described by an equation of the form

$$\tilde{E}^* = -a(T)/\tilde{V} \qquad (3.2.14)$$

where $a(T)$ depends on temperature but not on volume.

The molar configurational Helmholtz free energy is found by combining (14) with (8) according to the equation

$$\tilde{A}^* = \tilde{E}^* - T\tilde{S}^* \qquad (3.2.15)$$

The pressure can then be found by differentiating with respect to volume. The result is the Eyring equation of state:

$$[p + a(T)/\tilde{V}^2][\tilde{V} - (\tilde{V}_0')^{1/3}\tilde{V}^{2/3}] = RT \qquad (3.2.16)$$

This equation is similar in form to the van der Waals equation except that the "excluded volume" depends on the actual volume $\tilde{V}$. The equation contains an arbitrary function of temperature $a(T)$ as well as the arbitrary constant $\tilde{V}_0'$; it is capable of giving a useful semiempirical description of the properties of liquids and gases.[5]

3.3 *A Simple Hole Theory*[6]

When most substances melt the density and the apparent number of
nearest neighbours (as determined by X-ray or neutron diffraction)
decrease. As the temperature of the liquid is raised both density and
apparent number of nearest neighbours decrease still further. These
facts suggest that if we are to use a lattice picture of the structure of
liquids we ought to allow for the presence of vacant lattice sites or
holes. The presence of holes, and their more or less random distribution
on the lattice, would explain at least part of the disorder in liquids which
gives rise to the entropy increase on melting. Furthermore the presence
of holes would give a basis for understanding the relative ease of diffusion and flow in liquids in terms of a "vacancy diffusion" mechanism.
It was this latter consideration which originally led Eyring[7] to postulate
the presence of holes in liquids.

The additional disorder and entropy which arise in the hole theories
from the different distributions of holes on the lattice are described in
the cell theory as part of the communal entropy. If the hole theory
cells are so small that they cannot contain two molecules then by
describing all molecular configurations with either one molecule
or no molecule in each cell we must describe the whole of configuration
space. But we are obliged to use the Einstein model approximation of
independent motion, so that we do *not* describe all the molecular
configurations corresponding to each distribution of holes on the lattice,
and we cannot be certain of including the whole of the communal
entropy. In fact hole theories give the correct value for the entropy of
the perfect gas, so that the whole of the communal entropy is included
in the low density limit. But at high densities the proportion of holes
becomes very small and the predictions of the hole theories are very
close to those of cell theories.

In the cell theory thermal expansion is explained by an increase in
the cell size or lattice parameter. In a hole theory we could if we
wished postulate that the cell size remains constant (independent of
density and temperature) so that the whole of the thermal expansion is
due to the increasing number of holes. Alternatively we could suppose
that both the cell size (lattice parameter) and the number of holes
vary, and that the cell size at each density and temperature is to be
chosen to give the lowest value of the free energy. Both of these possibilities have been investigated (see chapter 7). In the simple theory to
be developed here the cell size will be assumed constant.

We shall consider a fixed lattice of cells, each cell having volume q.

The co-ordination number of the lattice (number of nearest-neighbour cells) will be denoted by z. We consider N molecules and N_0 holes (unoccupied cells) distributed over $(N + N_0)$ cells of the lattice, so that the total volume V and volume per molecule v are given by

$$V = Nv$$
$$= (N + N_0)q \qquad (3.3.1)$$

In the cell theory of course the volume of the cell and the volume per molecule are equal; here they are related by (1). We shall suppose that the attractive forces are such that the mutual potential energy of two molecules is $-\epsilon$ if they lie at the centres of a nearest-neighbour pair of cells, and that the variation of potential energy as the molecules move in the cells can be dealt with by evaluating the "free volume" as in section 3.2. Strictly speaking the free volume for a given molecule must depend on the number and arrangement of its neighbours, so that we should define a symbol $v_f^{i\lambda}$, representing the volume available to the centre of molecule i in the arrangement λ of molecules in the cells. Then corresponding to (3.2.1) we should have the equation

$$Q(N,\ V,\ T) = (1/N!) \sum_{\lambda}{}' \left(\prod_{i=1}^{N} v_f^{i\lambda} \right) \exp\left(M_{\lambda}\epsilon/kT \right) \qquad (3.3.2)$$

where M_{λ} is the number of nearest-neighbour pairs of occupied cells in the arrangement λ of molecules in the cells and $\sum_{\lambda}{}'$ means "sum over all arrangements λ of the N molecules in $N + N_0$ cells such that each cell contains one molecule or no molecule". In fact we shall make here the crude approximation of treating $v_f^{i\lambda}$ as a function of temperature alone, so that (2) becomes

$$Q(N,\ V,\ T) = (v_f^N/N!) \sum_{\lambda}{}' \exp\left(M_{\lambda}\epsilon/kT \right) \qquad (3.3.3)$$

We shall evaluate the summation in (3) by an approximation equivalent to the Bragg-Williams approximation for order–disorder problems (Cernuschi and Eyring[6] used the more accurate Bethe approximation; see chapter 7). We replace M_{λ} by its *a priori* average over all the arrangements of molecules in the cells, which is $\frac{1}{2}zN^2/(N_0 + N)$. Since the total number of arrangements is $(N_0 + N)!/N_0!$ this approximation gives

$$Q = \frac{(N_0 + N)!}{N_0!\,N!}\, v_f^N \exp\left[zN^2\epsilon/2kT(N_0 + N) \right] \qquad (3.3.4)$$

The Helmholtz free energy is $-kT \ln Q$; using (1), N_0 can be eliminated and the pressure can be calculated by differentiation:

$$p = -\partial A^*/\partial V$$

$$= \frac{kT}{q}\left[-\ln\left(1-\frac{Nq}{V}\right) - \left(\frac{z\epsilon}{2kT}\right)\left(\frac{Nq}{V}\right)^2\right] \qquad (3.3.5)$$

The free volume v_f does not appear in the expression for the pressure since v_f was assumed to be independent of density. Three isotherms calculated from (5) are shown in Fig. 3.1. At low temperatures ($z\epsilon/2kT$

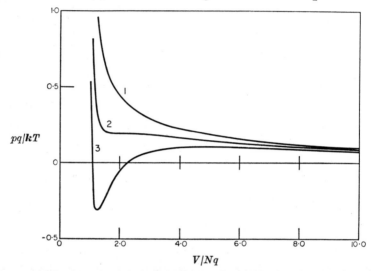

FIG. 3.1. Pressure–volume isotherms calculated from simple hole theory (equation (3.3.5)). Curve 1, $\dfrac{z\epsilon}{2kT} = 1$. Curve 2, $\dfrac{z\epsilon}{2kT} = 2$. Curve 3, $\dfrac{z\epsilon}{2kT} = 3$.

large) the isotherms have sigmoid form with branches corresponding to condensed and gaseous phases; at high temperatures they are monotonic. The critical temperature is given by

$$\frac{kT_c}{\epsilon} = \frac{z}{4} \qquad (3.3.6)$$

For a close-packed arrangement of the cells with $z = 12$ this gives $kT_c/\epsilon = 3$. This is much higher than the experimental values, since kT_c/ϵ is about 1·3 for inert gases. The discrepancy is due primarily to the crude approximation of treating the free volume as independent of the number and arrangement of neighbouring molecules (the Bethe approximation gives $kT_c/\epsilon = 2\cdot74$ for $z = 12$).

3.4 *The Order–Disorder Theory of Melting*

The theories described so far allow for the existence of only one condensed phase, which seems in fact to resemble a solid more than a liquid. Insofar as the simple cell and hole theories are theories of liquids they are not sufficiently precise to distinguish the properties of the liquid from those of the solid. To allow for the existence of solid and liquid phases within the framework of a lattice picture Lennard-Jones and Devonshire[8,9] proposed a model in which N molecules are distributed on a lattice of $2N$ sites divided into two interpenetrating sub-lattices α and β each of N sites. In this model the solid corresponds to an ordered state in which almost all of the molecules lie on one of the two sub-lattices, while the liquid corresponds to a disordered state in which the molecules are distributed without long-range order over the whole $2N$ lattice sites.

We consider two interpenetrating face-centred cubic lattices α and β in which each α site has six neighbouring β sites and vice versa. The combined lattice is a simple cubic lattice. As in section 3.3 the configuration integral can be written in the form

$$Q = (1/N\,!) \sum_\lambda{}'' \left(\prod_{i=1}^{N} v_{\mathrm{f}}^{i\lambda}\right) \exp\left(-U'_\lambda/kT\right) \qquad (3.4.1)$$

where $v_{\mathrm{f}}^{i\lambda}$ is the free volume for molecule i in arrangement λ and U'^λ is the energy of arrangement λ when all the molecules are at their cell centres or lattice sites. The summation $\sum_\lambda{}''$ means "sum over all arrangements λ of the N molecules with one molecule or no molecule at each of the $2N$ lattice sites". We shall suppose again that $v_{\mathrm{f}}^{i\lambda}$ does not depend on the number or arrangement of the neighbouring molecules but is in this case a function of temperature and density alone. If U'_0 denotes the energy of the completely ordered arrangement in which all the molecules occupy one sub-lattice, then (1) may be written

$$Q = \frac{v_{\mathrm{f}}^N}{N\,!} \exp\left(-U'_0/kT\right) \sum_\lambda{}'' \exp\left[-(U'_\lambda - U'_0)/kT\right]$$

$$ \qquad (3.4.2)$$

$$= \frac{Q_0}{N\,!} \sum_\lambda{}'' \exp\left[-(U'_\lambda - U'_0)kT\right]$$

where Q_0 is the configuration integral for the ordered arrangement.

We shall suppose that the interaction energy is W' for two molecules on adjacent sites of *different* sub-lattices (nearest neighbours in the combined lattice) and W'' for two molecules on adjacent sites of the *same* sub-lattice (second nearest neighbours in the combined lattice), and that interactions between further neighbours can be neglected.

We shall evaluate the summation in (2) using the method of Bragg and Williams (Lennard-Jones and Devonshire[8] also used Bethe's method, finding similar results). In this method the energy U'_λ of each arrangement λ with N_α molecules on α sites and N_β on β sites is approximated by the average energy of all arrangements with the same partition of molecules between the sub-lattices. This gives

$$U'_\lambda = \tfrac{1}{2}N_\alpha \left(6\frac{N_\beta}{N} W' + 12 \frac{N_\alpha}{N} W''\right) + \tfrac{1}{2}N_\beta \left(6\frac{N_\alpha}{N} W' + 12 \frac{N_\beta}{N} W''\right)$$

$$(3.4.3)$$

since on the average $6N_\beta/N$ of the six β sites and $12N_\alpha/N$ of the twelve α sites neighbouring a given α site are occupied, with corresponding results for β sites. Combining (3) with the expression

$$U'_0 = \tfrac{1}{2}N \cdot 12W'' \qquad (3.4.4)$$

we find

$$U'_\lambda - U'_0 = 6NW\frac{N_\alpha}{N}\left(1 - \frac{N_\alpha}{N}\right) \qquad (3.4.5)$$

where W is $W' - 2W''$. Since the number of ways of arranging N (distinguishable) molecules with N_α on α sites and N_β on β sites is given by

$$g = N\,!(N\,!/N_\alpha\,!N_\beta\,!)^2 \qquad (3.4.6)$$

the configuration integral is given by

$$Q = Q_0 \sum_{N_\alpha} \left[\frac{N\,!}{N_\alpha\,!(N - N_\alpha)\,!}\right]^2 \exp\left[-x(1 - x)6NW/kT\right] \quad (3.4.7)$$

in which x is N_α/N.

The summation over N_α in (7) can be replaced by its maximum term without appreciable error in the calculated free energy. The value of N_α giving the maximum term is found by equating the derivative with respect to N_α to zero; this leads to the result

$$\frac{6W(2x - 1)}{2kT} = \ln\left(\frac{x}{1 - x}\right) \qquad (3.4.8)$$

This equation is satisfied by $x = \tfrac{1}{2}$, and when $6W/2kT$ is less than 2 this is the only solution. When $6W/2kT$ is greater than 2 the solution $x = \tfrac{1}{2}$ gives a *minimum* and there are two maxima at $x = x_0$ and

$x = 1 - x_0$ with x_0 greater than $\frac{1}{2}$. Thus, when $6W/2kT$ is less than 2 the system is disordered with equal numbers of molecules on α and β lattices; when $6W/2kT$ is greater than 2 it is partially ordered with N_α and N_β unequal. The existence of two solutions symmetrical about $x = \frac{1}{2}$ reflects the symmetry between the α and β lattices.

The Helmholtz free energy is given by

$$A^* = -kT \ln Q$$
$$= A' + A'' \tag{3.4.9}$$

where

$$A' = -kT \ln Q_0 \tag{3.4.10}$$

$$A'' = -6NWx(1 - x) - 2NkT[x \ln x + (1 - x) \ln (1 - x)] \tag{3.4.11}$$

Thus A' is the free energy of the completely ordered system while A'' is the contribution of the disorder to the free energy. In (11) x is to be understood as the appropriate solution of (8) for the given value of W/kT.

It is to be expected that W, the difference between α–β and α–α interaction energies, will depend on the lattice parameter and therefore on the density. Since W is likely to be determined largely by the repulsive forces it is reasonable that for 12–6 molecules it should be taken as inversely proportional to the fourth power of the volume:

$$W = W_0(V_0/V)^4 \tag{3.4.12}$$

where
$$V_0 = N\sigma^3 \tag{3.4.13}$$

If the constant W_0 and the free energy A' of the completely ordered system were known then the free energy A^* of the actual disordered or partially disordered system could be calculated. For A' and the corresponding pressure $p' = -\partial A'/\partial V$, Lennard-Jones and Devonshire used values calculated from their cell theory (see chapter 4). For an assumed value of W_0 they could therefore calculate the pressure p using the equations

$$p = p' + p'' \tag{3.4.14}$$

$$p'' = -\partial A''/\partial V \tag{3.4.15}$$

The qualitative behaviour of the calculated pressures is shown in Fig. 3.2. At the point P the critical value of W for which $6W/2kT$ is 2 is attained. To the left of P there is partial long-range order (N_α and N_β unequal); to the right of P there is no long-range order ($N_\alpha = N_\beta$).

D

The form of the isotherm shows that for a certain pressure two condensed phases exist in equilibrium. The partially ordered denser phase is identified with the solid, the disordered less dense phase with the liquid. The equilibrium pressure can be determined by the criterion of equal areas or by equating chemical potentials.

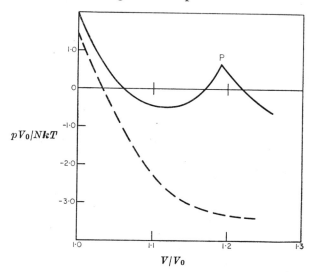

Fig. 3.2. Qualitative behaviour of pressure calculated from order–disorder theory. Solid curve, total pressure; dotted curve, pressure for fully ordered arrangement. (Reproduced with permission from *Proc. Roy. Soc.*).

To determine the constant W_0 Lennard-Jones and Devonshire followed the semiempirical procedure of adjusting W_0 so that the zero-pressure freezing point coincided with its experimental value. For argon this led to the result $W_0 = 0\cdot928\epsilon$, where ϵ is the minimum energy of intereaction of two argon atoms. A similar calculation using the method of Bethe for the order–disorder problem[9] led to the slightly different value $1\cdot048\epsilon$. With W_0 known the volume change on melting $\Delta_m V$ and the molar entropy of melting $\Delta_m \tilde{S}$ could be calculated as well as the melting pressure p_m at other temperatures and the coefficient of expansion of the liquid. The calculated values of these quantities proved to be in good agreement with their experimental values (see Table 3.1).

The agreement between the theoretical estimates and the experimental quantities in Table 3.1 is impressive. As a semiempirical theory, with W_0 determined to give the correct zero-pressure freezing point, the order–disorder theory fits these experimental facts very well. From the fundamental point of view the position is less satisfactory.

In this theory the liquid state is described in terms of a completely disordered arrangement of molecules on a simple cubic lattice with half the lattice sites unoccupied, and the crude approximation that the free volume is independent of the number and arrangement of neighbours is made. However, a more accurate treatment of this model for the liquid would lead to equilibrium volumes very much larger than the experimental liquid volumes[10]; if the nearest-neighbour distance remained the same the volume of the half-occupied simple cubic lattice would exceed the volume of a face-centred cubic lattice by a factor of $2\sqrt{2}$. Thus it must be assumed that the actual situation is entirely changed by local distortions of the lattice, and that the semiempirical determination of W_0 is an indirect way of accounting for this fact.

TABLE 3.1

Melting properties of argon

	Method of Bethe	Method of Bragg and Williams	Experimental
W_0/ϵ	1·048	0·928	—
$\Delta_m V/V$	0·128	0·135	0·12
$\Delta_m \tilde{S}$ (83·8°K)	1·74R	1·70R	1·66R
p_m(90·3°K)/dyn cm^{-2}	294 × 10^6	286 × 10^6	291 × 10^6
$(1/V)(\partial V/\partial T)$(liquid)/°K^{-1}	0·0049	0·0040	0·0045

It is also found that the minimum in the calculated pressure–volume isotherm disappears above a critical temperature given approximately by $1\cdot1\epsilon/k$. Above this temperature the theory predicts that there should be no discontinuous change in volume or entropy on melting; the melting transition becomes a higher-order transition. Bridgman[11] has measured the volume change on melting and calculated the latent heat for argon up to 6000 kgf/cm^2 and 193·1°K; this temperature is about $1\cdot6\epsilon/k$. At the highest pressures there is no noticeable change in latent heat, and the product of pressure and volume change has become almost constant. The Monte Carlo calculations (chapter 2) indicate that at a temperature of $2\cdot74\epsilon/k$ there are still discontinuities in volume and entropy on melting. Thus the theoretical prediction of a critical temperature above which the discontinuities vanish is apparently contradicted by the facts. It seems that there is a more fundamental difference between liquid and solid than is envisaged in the order–disorder theory.

3.5   *A Simple Tunnel Theory*

The discussion given so far indicates that the task of basing a satisfactory theory of liquids on a regular lattice model may prove at best difficult and at worst impossible. It is natural to ask whether one could imagine an *irregular* lattice model, based on a model structure which has sufficient regularity or simplicity to permit a simple description but which is disordered in a more fundamental way than the cell or hole models permit. One such model is the "tunnel" model[12] which is *one-dimensionally* disordered.

Consider a set of rigid spherical beads sliding freely on a straight wire. We may regard this as a one-dimensional rigid-sphere fluid; the beads may take any positions on the wire provided no two of them are separated by a distance less than the diameter. Now imagine a number of such wires with beads on them stacked parallel to each other, but not so closely that the beads can no longer slide freely—the distance between adjacent wires is to be not less than the diameter of the beads. Looking *along* the wires we should see a two-dimensional pattern formed by the ends of the wires. The most dense packing of this kind is realized when this pattern forms a two-dimensional close-packed structure with each wire surrounded symmetrically by six others. The beads on a given wire move within a kind of "tunnel" whose walls are formed by the beads of the six neighbouring wires. These tunnels are analogous to the cells in the cell model. Instead of one molecule in a cell we have a whole line of molecules in a tunnel. The essential disorder in the model arises from the fact that the positions of beads on different wires are independent.

Now imagine that we remove one of the wires, leaving the beads in position. This will make very little difference to the motion of the beads *along* the tunnel; they will still be constrained to move almost one-dimensionally by the beads on the neighbouring wires. However, they will now be able to perform vibrations of comparatively small amplitude transversely to the tunnel axis. The *transverse* and *longitudinal* motions should be nearly independent. To a good approximation the total configuration integral should be the *product* of configuration integrals for longitudinal and transverse motions. The configuration integral for the longitudinal motion, which is one-dimensional, can be evaluated exactly. The configuration integral for the transverse motion can be evaluated in terms of a "free area" exactly analogous to the "free volume" in the cell model. Corresponding to the Einstein approximation of independent motion in the cell model we suppose in considering the motion of the molecules in one tunnel that the molecules in neighbouring tunnels remain on their respective tunnel axes. However, we account correctly for the correlated motions of molecules in the same tunnel.

The advantage of this model over cell and hole models is basically that it permits a more extensive sampling of configuration space, in regions not necessarily "close" to regular lattice configurations. Density fluctuations are permitted since the molecules may take up any positions along the tunnel axis, and these include small fluctuations as well as the relatively gross fluctuations described in the hole theories by empty cells. We shall see that the tunnel theory gives the correct result for the entropy of a perfect gas, so that the whole of the communal entropy is included at least in the low-density limit.

We shall develop the tunnel theory for rigid spherical molecules. We imagine the volume V divided into a number K of hexagonal cylinders arranged in close packing. The cross-sectional area of each cylinder is $\sqrt{3} \cdot r^2/2$ where r is the distance between the centres of neighbouring cylinders. If each cylinder contains M molecules and is of length lM then the total number of molecules N is equal to KM, and

$$\frac{V}{N} = \frac{\sqrt{3}}{2} lr^2 \tag{3.5.1}$$

Following the arguments set out above we take as our approximation to the configuration integral

$$Q(N, V) = (1/N\,!)[N\,!/(M\,!)^K]\, A_f^N \left[\int_0^{lM} \dots \int_0^{lM} \exp\left(-U'/kT\right) \mathrm{d}z_1 \dots \mathrm{d}z_M \right]^K \tag{3.5.2}$$

In (1) U' is the potential energy of the one-dimensional system of M molecules in length lM; it is $+\infty$ if $(z_i - z_j)$ is less than D for any i and j, and zero otherwise. The "free area" is denoted by A_f.

The factor $N\,!/(M\,!)^K$ is the number of ways of distributing the N molecules with M in each cylinder. Strictly we should sum over *all* distributions of the molecules in the cylinders, not just those with exactly M in each cylinder. However, because M is very large the resulting corrections would be entirely negligible. This is quite different from the situation in the cell theory where if we wish to evaluate the communal entropy we must take explicit account of the possibility of cells being occupied by 0, 1, 2 ... molecules.

The integral appearing in (1) is closely related to the configuration integral $Q'(M, lM)$ for a one-dimensional system of M molecules in length lM. In fact we have

$$Q'(M, lM) = (1/M\,!) \int_0^{lM} \cdots \int_0^{lM} \exp\left(-U'/kT\right) dz_1 \ldots dz_M \quad (3.5.3)$$

For rigid spheres (see chapter 9) this is known to be given by

$$Q'(M, lM) = e^M (l - D)^M \quad (3.5.4)$$

Substituting this in (2) we find

$$Q(N, V) = e^N(l - D)^N A_f^N \quad (3.5.5)$$

The free area A_f is the average cross-sectional area available to the centre of each molecule. At high densities this is of course less than $\sqrt{3}.r^2/2$ because much of the area is excluded by the molecules in neighbouring tunnels. However, in the low density limit A_f becomes equal to $\sqrt{3}.r^2/2$ and D becomes negligible compared with l, so that (5) becomes

$$Q(N, V) = e^N l^N (\sqrt{3}.r^2/2)^N$$
$$= e^N (V/N)^N \quad (3.5.6)$$

This is the correct result for the perfect gas; the cell theory by contrast omits the factor e^N. This result is independent of l and r, provided that they satisfy (1). At high densities we shall choose the values of l and r which maximize the configuration integral Q subject to the restriction imposed by (1), since these are presumably the values which the system would adopt.

For high densities we shall consider two different approximations to the free area A_f. The first approximation ($T1$) is exactly analogous to the "smearing" approximation used in section 3.2:

$$A_f = \pi(r - D)^2 \quad (3.5.7)$$

The second approximation ($T2$), which should be more accurate, replaces D in (7) by the average closest distance of approach of a molecule of diameter D to the line of centres of a line of similar molecules equally spaced with spacing l:

$$A_f = \pi(r - D')^2 \quad (3.5.8)$$

$$D' = (D^2/l)[\arcsin (l/2D) + (l/2D)\sqrt{(1 - l^2/4D^2)}] \quad (3.5.9)$$

Using the approximation $T1$ (equation (7)) we find

$$Q(N, V) = [\pi(r - D)^2(l - D)e]^N \quad (3.5.10)$$

t is easy to show that Q is a maximum subject to (1) when r and l are qual, so that

$$r = l = (2V/N\sqrt{3})^{1/3} \tag{3.5.11}$$

he Helmholtz free energy and the pressure are given by

$$A^* = -kT \ln Q \tag{3.5.12}$$

$$p = -\partial A^*/\partial V$$

$$= (NkT/V)/[1 - (3/2)^{1/6}(V_0/V)^{1/3}] \tag{3.5.13}$$

or details of the calculation using the approximation $T2$ we refer to ie original publication.[12]

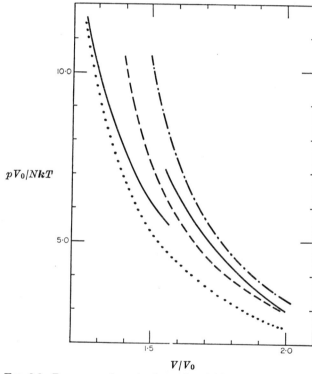

pV_0/NkT

V/V_0

FIG. 3.3. Pressure–volume isotherm for rigid spherical molecules. Monte Carlo results shown thus ——————, free volume theory thus $\cdots\cdots$, tunnel theory $T1$ thus $-\cdot-\cdot-\cdot$ and $T2$ thus $-\,-\,-$. (Reproduced with permission from *Australian J. Chem.*).

The calculated pressures are shown in Fig. 3.3, with results calculated y the molecular dynamics method for comparison. The tunnel theory alues are satisfactorily close to the *fluid* branch of the isotherm; the alues calculated with the approximation $T2$ seem to be approaching the (extrapolated) *fluid* isotherm at high densities in much the same way as the cell theory values approach the *solid* isotherm.

The most serious objection to the tunnel model is its anisotropic character. As far as the local molecular environment is concerned this is probably not a serious weakness. There is no reason to suppose that the instantaneous environment of a particular molecule is exactly spherically symmetrical, and the *local* configurations permitted by the tunnel model could not easily be distinguished from purely random configurations. Furthermore the tunnel model predicts a radial distribution function for liquid argon in good agreement with experiment (see chapter 10). On a larger scale the model does restrict the accessible regions of configuration space to those in the neighbourhood of "beads on wires" configurations. This is possibly less drastic than the restriction to the neighbourhood of regular lattice configurations imposed by the cell and hole theories.

REFERENCES

1. BUEHLER, R. J., WENTORF, R. H., HIRSCHFELDER, J. O. and CURTISS, C. F., *J. Chem. Phys.* 1951, **19**, 61.
2. BERNAL, J. D., *Nature, Lond.* 1960, **185**, 68.
3. EYRING, H. and HIRSCHFELDER, J. O., *J. phys. Chem.* 1937, **41**, 249.
4. HIRSCHFELDER, J. O., *J. chem. Educ.* 1939, **16**, 540.
5. HIRSCHFELDER, J. O., CURTISS, C. F. and BIRD, R. B., *Molecular Theory of Gases and Liquids*, p. 282, Chapman & Hall, London, 1954.
6. CERNUSCHI, F. and EYRING, H., *J. chem. Phys.* 1939, **7**, 547.
7. EYRING, H., *J. chem. Phys.* 1936, **4**, 283.
8. LENNARD-JONES, J. E. and DEVONSHIRE, A. F., *Proc. roy. Soc.* 1939, **A169**, 317.
9. LENNARD-JONES, J. E. and DEVONSHIRE, A. F., *Proc. roy. Soc.* 1939, **A170**, 464.
10. DE BOER, J., *Proc. roy. Soc.* 1952, **A215**, 4.
11. BRIDGMAN, P. W., *Phys. Rev.* 1934, **46**, 930.
12. BARKER, J. A., *Australian J. Chem.* 1960, **13**, 187.

CHAPTER 4

THE THEORY OF LENNARD-JONES AND DEVONSHIRE

4.1 *The Cell Theory*

The possibility of basing a theoretical description of real liquids and compressed gases on the cell model was first investigated in detail by Lennard-Jones and Devonshire. In two papers[1,2] these authors showed how to make consistent calculations of thermodynamic properties based on the cell model for molecules interacting according to realistic potential functions, in particular the 12–6 potential. They found that the cell theory predicted the existence of "condensed" and "gaseous" phases at low temperatures, and that the calculated densities and boiling points of the condensed phase were reasonably close to experimental liquid densities and boiling points for substances to which the 12–6 potential could be expected to apply. They were, however, even closer to the corresponding properties of the solids. Lennard-Jones and Devonshire also found that the cell theory predicted the existence of a critical isotherm at a temperature close to the experimental critical temperature, although the calculated critical pressure and density differed from their experimental values.

In later papers[3–6] Lennard-Jones and Devonshire indicated that they regarded the cell model as more properly a model for *solids*, and they explained the differences between solids and liquids in terms of their order–disorder theory of melting. We have seen in section 3.4 that the latter theory gives a semiempirical account of some of the experimental facts but cannot be regarded as a satisfactory fundamental theory of the liquid state. This later aspect of the work of Lennard-Jones and Devonshire has not been followed up as fully as the earlier work, and it has become customary to describe the cell theory of the first two papers as "the theory of Lennard-Jones and Devonshire", abbreviated to "L-J-D theory".

In making comparisons with experiment we shall find that the L-J-D theory appears to describe solids and not liquids. It is in fact an excellent theory of solids in the temperature range where quantum effects are not important. This is not surprising since the theory uses essentially the Einstein model with full correction for anharmonicity. One might have hoped that the theory would describe *both* solids and liquids in appropriate temperature ranges. This is not the case. Above the melting point the theory describes a solid phase which is metastable (at low pressures).

In spite of this the theory is of fundamental importance in the theory of liquids, because effectively all progress towards a satisfactory lattice or structural theory of liquids has arisen from attempts to justify or improve the L-J-D theory. The theoretical and mathematical techniques developed by Lennard-Jones and Devonshire for dealing with the cell model are used in all lattice theories. Furthermore the L-J-D theory may validly be regarded as an approximate theory of fluids since from some points of view the thermodynamic differences between solids and fluids are small, particularly if the fluid and the solid are considered at the same density. In the last twenty years many discussions of experimental data for liquids and solutions have been based on the L-J-D theory.

If the L-J-D theory actually describes the solid phase, the fact that it predicts a critical isotherm at a temperature close to the observed liquid–gas critical temperature requires explanation, since it is certain experimentally that there is no solid–gas critical temperature in this temperature range (cf. section 3.4). The explanation seems to be that the phase transition which disappears at the critical point given by the theory is neither the solid–gas transition nor the liquid–gas transition, but a hypothetical transition from a condensed ordered phase to an expanded ordered phase ("expanded solid"). The prediction of a critical isotherm is based on using the L-J-D theory, with its restriction that each cell contains one molecule, for both condensed and expanded phases, so that both phases are in a sense solid-like. This point is discussed in detail in section 4.6.

4.2 *Assumptions*

The fundamental assumptions of the cell model are: (i) that the available volume may be divided into identical cells, one for each molecule, and that only configurations in which every cell contains one molecule need be considered; (ii) that the cells can be chosen so that their centres form a regular lattice; (iii) that the molecules can be regarded as moving independently in their cells. The second assumption is required in order that the distance between cell centres can be related to the density. The third is required to make evaluation of the configuration integral practicable. It implies that the potential energy of the system can be approximated by a sum of terms each depending on the position of just one molecule. If this were not so the force on one molecule would depend on the position of another and the motions of the molecules would not be independent. Thus we assume

$$U = U_0' + \sum_i \psi_i(\mathbf{r}_i) \tag{4.2.1}$$

where $\mathbf{r}_i$ is the vector displacement of molecule i from the centre of its cell and U_0' is a constant. If all the cells are identical the functions ψ_i must also be identical so that we can drop the subscript. If U_0 is the potential energy when all molecules are at their cell centres then

$$U_0 = U_0' + \sum_i \psi(0) \tag{4.2.2}$$

so that (1) becomes

$$U = U_0 + \sum_i [\psi(\mathbf{r}_i) - \psi(0)] \tag{4.2.3}$$

It is clear from (3) that $[\psi(\mathbf{r}_i) - \psi(0)]$ is the change of potential energy when the molecule i moves from its cell centre to the point $\mathbf{r}_i$, with all other molecules remaining at their cell centres. Equation (3) has already been quoted in section 3.2. The purpose of the argument just given is to show that it follows unambiguously from the assumptions (i)–(iii). These assumptions and the errors they introduce are analysed in chapter 6.

With the potential energy approximated by (3) the configuration integral is given by

$$Q(N, V, T) = (1/N\,!) \sum{}' \exp\left(-U_0/kT\right)v_f^N$$
$$= \exp\left(-U_0/kT\right)v_f^N \tag{4.2.4}$$

The summation $\sum'$ in (4) is taken over all arrangements of the molecules with one in each cell, and the "free volume" v_f is defined by

$$v_f = \int \exp\left\{-[\psi(\mathbf{r}_i) - \psi(0)]/kT\right\} \, d\mathbf{r}_i \tag{4.2.5}$$

The integration in (5) is to be taken throughout the interior of the cell. We have not so far specified the precise form of the cell, except that its volume must be equal to the volume per molecule. We shall assume that the lattice of cell centres is a face-centred cubic lattice (cf. section 3.2). The most obvious choice for the cell shape is then the dodecahedron formed by the planes bisecting the lines drawn between nearest-neighbour lattice points. We shall see later that it is more convenient to replace this by a spherical cell.

4.3   Cell Field, Free Volume and Lattice Energy

Each molecule in its cell moves in a potential energy field defined by the function $[\psi(\mathbf{r}) - \psi(0)]$. If the potential energy function $u(R)$ for interaction of pairs of molecules is known this cell field can be calculated. In general it is a complicated function of the position of the molecule in the cell. Lennard-Jones and Devonshire proposed that this complicated function should be replaced by a spherically symmetrical function depending only on the distance ρ of the molecule from the centre of its cell, and calculated by averaging the potential energy over a sphere of radius ρ centred at the cell centre. The cell field derived in this way is identical with that derived by regarding the neighbouring molecules as "smeared" with uniform probability distribution over the surfaces of concentric spheres of appropriate radius. This smearing approximation is quite accurate, particularly at high densities (see chapter 6).

The "smeared" cell field can be calculated from the equation

$$[\psi(\rho) - \psi(0)] = \sum_j \frac{1}{2} \int_0^\pi [u(\sqrt{(a_j^2 + \rho^2 - 2\rho a_j \cos \theta_j)}) - u(a_j)] \sin \theta_j \, d\theta_j$$

$$(4.3.1)$$

The summation in (1) is taken over all cells surrounding the cell under consideration. If O_j is the centre of the cell j, and O is the centre of the cell under consideration and the molecule in the central cell is at the point P, then a_j is the distance OO_j and θ_j is the angle POO_j. In (1) we may group together the contributions arising from a particular shell of neighbours. Thus if the subscript n identifies the nth shell (nearest, second nearest ... neighbours with $n = 1, 2 \ldots$), (1) becomes

$$[\psi(\rho) - \psi(0)] = \sum_n m_n \cdot \frac{1}{2} \int_0^\pi [u(\sqrt{(a_n^2 + \rho^2 - 2\rho a_n \cos \theta)}) - u(a_n)] \times$$

$$\times \sin \theta \, d\theta \quad (4.3.2)$$

in which m_n is the number of nth neighbours and a_n the nth neighbour distance (measured from cell centre to cell centre). Values of m_n and a_n for the face-centred cubic lattice are listed in Table 4.1 (the values of a_n are given in terms of the nearest-neighbour distance a_1).

TABLE 4.1

Number and distance of neighbours in face-centred cubic lattice

Shell number n	1	2	3	4	5	6
Distance a_n	a_1	$a_1\sqrt{2}$	$a_1\sqrt{3}$	$a_1\sqrt{4}$	$a_1\sqrt{5}$	$a_1\sqrt{6}$
Number m_n	12	6	24	12	24	8

The integration in (2) can be performed readily for potential functions of the Lennard-Jones bireciprocal type by using the equation

$$\frac{1}{2}\int_0^\pi [\sqrt{(a^2 + \rho^2 - 2a\rho \cos\theta)}]^{-n} \sin\theta\, d\theta = \frac{1}{(2n-4)a\rho} \times$$

$$\times [(a-\rho)^{-n+2} - (a+\rho)^{-n+2}] \quad (4.3.3)$$

For the particular case of the 12–6 potential this leads to the results

$$[\psi(\rho) - \psi(0)] = 12\epsilon[(V_0/V)^4 L(y) - 2(V_0/V)^2 M(y)] \quad (4.3.4)$$

$$L(y) = \sum_n (m_n/m_1)(a_1/a_n)^{12} l(ya_1^2/a_n^2) \quad (4.3.5)$$

$$M(y) = \sum_n (m_n/m_1)(a_1/a_n)^6 m(ya_1^2/a_n^2) \quad (4.3.6)$$

in which y is $(\rho/a_1)^2$, V_0 is $N\sigma^3$ and the functions $l(y)$ and $m(y)$ are defined by

$$l(y) = (1 + 12y + 25{\cdot}2y^2 + 12y^3 + y^4)(1-y)^{-10} - 1 \quad (4.3.7)$$

$$m(y) = (1+y)(1-y)^{-4} - 1 \quad (4.3.8)$$

In calculating the free volume using these results it is much more convenient to use a spherical cell than the dodecahedral cell described above. At sufficiently high densities (roughly speaking densities greater than the critical density[7]) the integrand in (4.2.5) is effectively zero when ρ/a_1 is equal to or greater than 0·5, so that the error involved in replacing the dodecahedral cell by a sphere of radius $0{\cdot}5a_1$ or by a slightly larger sphere are negligible. Lennard-Jones and Devonshire[1,2] actually used a sphere of radius $0{\cdot}5a_1$; Wentorf et al.[7] used a sphere of radius $0{\cdot}55267a_1$, since the volume of this sphere is equal to the volume per molecule. With the latter value of the cell radius the free volume is given by

$$v_f = 2\pi a_1^3 G$$

$$= 2\sqrt{2}.\pi(V/N)G \quad (4.3.9)$$

$$G = \int_0^{0{\cdot}30544} y^{1/2} \exp\{-[\psi(\rho) - \psi(0)]/kT\}\, dy \quad (4.3.10)$$

Evaluation of the integral G requires numerical integration. Extensive tables of G as a function of (V/V_0) and (kT/ϵ) were prepared by Wentorf et al.[7] and by Fickett and Wood.[8] In these calculations the effects of nearest neighbours, second neighours and third neighbours were considered; that is the first three terms in (5) and (6) were retained. Earlier calculations of Lennard-Jones and Devonshire,[1,2] Hill[9] and Prigogine and Gariakin[10] considered only the effects of nearest neighbours. The tabulations also include values of integrals g_L and g_M related to G and defined by

$$g_L = \int_0^{0\cdot30544} y^{1/2} L(y) \exp\{-[\psi(\rho) - \psi(0)]/kT\}\, dy \qquad (4.3.11)$$

$$g_M = \int_0^{0\cdot30544} y^{1/2} M(y) \exp\{-[\psi(\rho) - \psi(0)]/kT\}\, dy \qquad (4.3.12)$$

The derivations of G with respect to volume and temperature can be evaluated in terms of g_L and g_M, since

$$V\frac{\partial \ln G}{\partial V} = \frac{48\epsilon}{kT}\left[\left(\frac{V_0}{V}\right)^4 \frac{g_L}{G} - \left(\frac{V_0}{V}\right)^2 \frac{g_M}{G}\right] \qquad (4.3.13)$$

$$T\frac{\partial \ln G}{\partial T} = \frac{12\epsilon}{kT}\left[\left(\frac{V_0}{V}\right)^4 \frac{g_L}{G} - 2\left(\frac{V_0}{V}\right)^2 \frac{g_M}{G}\right] \qquad (4.3.14)$$

These results may be verified using (4) and (10)–(12).

The lattice energy U_0 is the potential energy when all molecules lie at their lattice sites. It can therefore be evaluated by performing a lattice summation:

$$U_0 = \tfrac{1}{2}N \sum_{n=1}^{\infty} m_n u(a_n) \qquad (4.3.15)$$

For the 12–6 potential the required lattice sums have been evaluated by Lennard-Jones and Ingham;[11] the lattice energy is found to be

$$U_0 = 6N\epsilon[1\cdot0109(V_0/V)^4 - 2\cdot4090(V_0/V)^2] \qquad (4.3.16)$$

4.4   The Thermodynamic Functions

We shall now confine our attention to the 12–6 potential. Using (4.3.9) and (4.3.16) the configurational Helmholtz free energy is found to be given by

$$\frac{A^*}{NkT} = \frac{6\epsilon}{kT}\left[1\cdot0109\left(\frac{V_0}{V}\right)^4 - 2\cdot4090\left(\frac{V_0}{V}\right)^2\right] - \ln\left[2\sqrt{2.\pi}\left(\frac{V}{N}\right)G\right] \qquad (4.4.1)$$

By use of (4.3.13) and (4.3.14) the pressure and the configurational tropy and energy can be calculated by differentiating with respect to and V. The results are

$$\frac{V}{kT} = 1 - \frac{12\epsilon}{kT}\left[2 \cdot 4090\left(\frac{V_0}{V}\right)^2 - 2 \cdot 0219\left(\frac{V_0}{V}\right)^4\right]$$

$$- \frac{48\epsilon}{kT}\left[\left(\frac{V_0}{V}\right)^2\frac{g_M}{G} - \left(\frac{V_0}{V}\right)^4\frac{g_L}{G}\right] \quad (4.4.2)$$

$$\frac{*}{kT} = \frac{6\epsilon}{kT}\left[1 \cdot 0109\left(\frac{V_0}{V}\right)^4 - 2 \cdot 4090\left(\frac{V_0}{V}\right)^2\right]$$

$$+ \frac{12\epsilon}{kT}\left[\left(\frac{V_0}{V}\right)^4\frac{g_L}{G} - 2\left(\frac{V_0}{V}\right)^2\frac{g_M}{G}\right] \quad (4.4.3)$$

$$\frac{S*}{Vk} = \ln\left[2\sqrt{2 \cdot \pi}\left(\frac{V}{N}\right)G\right] + \left(\frac{12\epsilon}{kT}\right)\left[\left(\frac{V_0}{V}\right)^4\frac{g_L}{G} - 2\left(\frac{V_0}{V}\right)^2\frac{g_M}{G}\right] \quad (4.4.4)$$

Wentorf et al.[7] and Wood and Fickett[8] give extensive tables of $'/NkT$ and $E*/N\epsilon$ as functions of V/V_0 and kT/ϵ (the configurational ergy $E*$ is equal to the "excess" energy E' which these papers actually ,, since the configurational energy for the ideal gas is zero). They o tabulate the configurational (or excess) heat capacity at constant lume, derived by numerical differentiation of the E' values.

From (4) the excess entropy is given by

$$\frac{S'}{Nk} = \ln\left[2\sqrt{2 \cdot \pi}G/e\right] + \frac{12\epsilon}{kT}\left[\left(\frac{V_0}{V}\right)^4\frac{g_L}{G} - 2\left(\frac{V_0}{V}\right)^2\frac{g_M}{G}\right] \quad (4.4.5)$$

ce the configurational entropy of a perfect gas is given by

$$\frac{S*}{Nk} = \ln\left(\frac{eV}{N}\right) \quad (4.4.6)$$

ntorf et al.[7] and Wood and Fickett[8] tabulate values of S'/Nk which calculated by omitting the e in the first term in (5). Thus to find ues of S'/Nk as given by (5) it is necessary to subtract 1 from the ulated values. The tabulated values are in fact based on the assump- n that the "communal entropy" is Nk, whereas we are assuming e that the communal entropy is zero—that is we are following sistently the idea that each cell contains one molecule (see chapters nd 7).

Pressure–volume isotherms calculated from (2) have sigmoid form low temperatures, indicating the possibility of equilibrium between "condensed" and "expanded" phases. The critical temperature is found to be[7] $1 \cdot 30 \epsilon/k$, while the critical pressure and volume are $0 \cdot 434 N \epsilon/V_0$ and $1 \cdot 768 V_0$, respectively.

The zero-pressure volume of the condensed phase described by the L-J-D theory can be determined by setting p in (2) equal to zero and solving for (V/V_0). The energy, entropy and heat capacity can then be found by interpolation in the tables of Wentorf *et al.*[7] The values in Table 4.2 were determined by Hamann and David[12] by interpolation.

TABLE 4.2

Reduced properties of L-J-D condensed phase at zero pressure

Reduced temperature kT/ϵ	Reduced volume V/V_0	Reduced excess energy $E'/N\epsilon$	Reduced excess entropy S'/Nk	Reduced excess heat capacity C'_v/Nk
0·70	1·037	−7·323	−5·511	1·11
0·75	1·050	−7·188	−5·349	1·08
0·80	1·065	−7·063	−5·193	1·05
0·85	1·081	−6·928	−5·039	1·03
0·90	1·099	−6·779	−4·884	1·00
0·95	1·120	−6·610	−4·725	0·97
1·00	1·145	−6·410	−4·558	0·93

The vapour pressure p_s of the condensed phase can be determined from the equations

$$\tilde{A}_c^* + p_s \tilde{V}_c = \tilde{A}_g^* + p_s \tilde{V}_g \qquad (4.4.7)$$

$$p_s = -\partial \tilde{A}_c^*/\partial \tilde{V}_c \qquad (4.4.8)$$

$$p_s = -\partial \tilde{A}_g^*/\partial \tilde{V}_g \qquad (4.4.9)$$

In these equations the subscripts c and g refer to condensed phase and gas phase, respectively. The first equation expresses the equality of molar Gibbs free energies or chemical potentials in the two phases (the tilde is used here to denote a molar quantity), while (8) and (9) state that the phases are individually in equilibrium at the pressure p_s. We shall use the L-J-D theory to describe the condensed phase and the usual theory of imperfect gases to describe the gas phase. Approximate results may be obtained by neglecting gas imperfection and the effect of pressure on the condensed phase. With these approximations (7) and (9) lead to the result

$$RT \ln (p_s/kT) = \tilde{A}_c^0 \qquad (4.4.10)$$

where A_{c0}^* is the zero-pressure free energy of the condensed phase.

Vapour pressures calculated from (10) are listed as "perfect gas" values in Table 4.3.

TABLE 4.3

Reduced vapour pressures of L-J-D condensed phase

kT/ϵ	$\log_{10}(p_s V_0/N\epsilon)$ perfect gas	$\log_{10}(p_s V_0/N\epsilon)$ imperfect gas	kT/ϵ	$\log_{10}(p_s V_0/N\epsilon)$ perfect gas	$\log_{10}(p_s V_0/N\epsilon)$ imperfect gas
0·70	−2·755	−2·742	0·90	−1·659	−1·543
0·75	−2·420	−2·396	0·924	—	−1·417
0·80	−2·138	−2·098	0·95	−1·475	—
0·85	−1·890	−1·824	1·00	−1·297	—

Lennard-Jones and Devonshire[2] calculated vapour pressures from an equation similar to (10) except that they divided by a factor of e, corresponding to the assumption that the communal entropy in the condensed phase is Nk. They found that normal boiling temperatures calculated in this way were close to experimental values, in fact a few per cent higher than the experimental boiling temperatures for simple liquids. If the factor e corresponding to the communal entropy was omitted the calculated boiling points were still close to experimental values but a few per cent lower. Comparison of boiling points is a very insensitive way of testing the calculated vapour pressures; we shall make a detailed test in section 4.6.

More accurate values for the vapour pressure can be calculated if the term $p_s \tilde{V}_c$ in (9) is retained but the compressibility of the condensed phase is neglected so that $\tilde{A}_c^*$ and $\tilde{V}_c$ are replaced by $\tilde{A}_{c0}^*$ and $\tilde{V}_{c0}^*$, respectively; and if terms involving second and third virial coefficients are retained in the expression for $\tilde{A}_g^*$. Under these conditions (7) and (9) become

$$\tilde{A}_{c0}^* + p_s \tilde{V}_{c0} = -\ln(\tilde{V}_g/\tilde{N}) + 2B/\tilde{V}_g + 3C/2\tilde{V}_g^2 \quad (4.4.11)$$

$$p_s \tilde{V}_g/\tilde{N}kT = 1 + B/\tilde{V}_g + C/\tilde{V}_g^2 \quad (4.4.12)$$

where $\tilde{V}_{c0}$ is the zero-pressure molar volume of the condensed phase and $\tilde{V}_g$ is the gas-phase molar volume.

The second and third virial coefficients B and C can be found from tables of virial coefficients for the 12–6 potential[13], and (11) and (12) can then be solved simultaneously to give p_s and $\tilde{V}_g$. Values of p_s

E

derived in this way are listed as "imperfect gas" values in Table 4.3. For temperatures higher than $0.924\epsilon/k$ the equations (11) and (12) cannot be solved simultaneously. This fact is explained in section 4.6.

4.5   Comparison with Experiment

Of all substances the inert gases conform most closely to the model on which the L-J-D theoretical calculations are based. The properties of helium and to some extent those of neon are influenced by quantum effects which cannot of course be described by the classical L-J-D theory. For the heavier inert gases these effects are smaller. The thermodynamic properties of argon have been studied much more extensively than those of krypton or xenon. We shall therefore test the L-J-D theory by making a detailed comparison of its predictions with the experimental properties of argon.

The 12–6 formula apparently describes the interaction between argon atoms with considerable accuracy, since the values of ϵ and σ derived from low-temperature crystal properties are close to those derived from second virial coefficient measurements[14] (see, however, Guggenheim and McGlashan[15]). The theoretical predictions of the L-J-D theory are based on the assumption of additivity of molecular interactions (see (1.3.2)). Since this assumption probably does not apply exactly for argon there is some uncertainty in our comparisons. As far as the properties of solid and liquid argon near the triple point are concerned this uncertainty concerns only the *difference* between the non-additive effects at the triple point and at temperatures well below the triple point (since the 12–6 potential derived from gas measurements give essentially correct values for the crystal properties at low temperatures). It is not unreasonable to hope that this difference may be considerably smaller than the whole effect of non-additivity, which should itself be small. The point being made is that in adopting the 12–6 potential we may be using a slightly incorrect pair potential function to compensate for neglected non-additive effects in the crystal at low temperatures. This compensation, effective at low temperatures, should be at least partially effective at the not very different densities of the solid and liquid at the triple point.

For the 12–6 potential constants ϵ and σ for argon we shall adopt the values $119.8k$ and 3.405Å, respectively, found by Michels et al.[16] from measurements of second virial coefficients; we have already seen that these values are close to values derived from the low-temperature crystal properties. Experimental properties of liquid argon will be taken from the careful compilation given by Rowlinson[17] and those of solid argon from that of Dobbs and Jones.[14] Vapour pressures for liquid and solid argon are given by Clark et al.[18]

The triple point for argon is 83·82°K, giving $kT/\epsilon = 0\cdot700$. The vapour pressure at the triple point is so low that its effect on the properties of the condensed phases can be neglected. We shall therefore compare the properties of the zero-pressure condensed phase at $kT/\epsilon = 0\cdot7$ as predicted by the L-J-D theory with the reduced properties of solid and liquid argon at the triple point (Table 4.4).

TABLE 4.4

L-J-D condensed phase compared with solid and liquid argon at triple point ($kT/\epsilon = 0\cdot70$)

	Reduced volume V/V_0	Reduced excess energy $E'/N\epsilon$	Reduced excess entropy S'/Nk	Reduced excess heat capacity C'_v/Nk
L-J-D theory	1·037	−7·32	−5·51	1·11
experiment, solid argon	1·035	−7·14	−5·33	1·41
experiment, liquid argon	1·186	−5·96	−3·64	0·85

The L-J-D volume is strikingly close to the experimental solid volume, and about 15 per cent lower than the experimental liquid volume. The L-J-D energy and entropy are both much closer to the experimental solid values than to the experimental liquid values; the L-J-D energy and entropy are both in fact a little lower than the experimental solid values. The difference between the L-J-D entropy and the experimental entropy is roughly of the magnitude to be expected from the fact that the L-J-D theory uses the Einstein approximation of independent motion (see chapter 6). The position with regard to the heat capacity is less clear, since the L-J-D value lies roughly half-way between the experimental solid and liquid values. We should expect of course that the heat capacity would be rather sensitive to any error due to the Einstein approximation.

Unfortunately the comparison of the L-J-D values with experimental solid properties cannot be extended to a wider temperature range because L-J-D calculations have not been performed at lower temperatures and the solid is not stable at zero pressure at higher temperatures. However, Fig. 4.1, in which the L-J-D zero-pressure volumes and experimental solid and liquid volumes are plotted against temperature, indicates clearly that the L-J-D values are following the extrapolated solid curve rather than the liquid curve. Similar conclusions follow from the vapour pressures plotted in Fig. 4.2. Vapour pressures calculated from the L-J-D theory using (4.4.11) and (4.4.12) or (4.4.10) follow the extrapolated solid vapour pressure curve rather closely; they increase more rapidly with temperature than the liquid vapour pressures, corresponding to the more negative value of the energy.

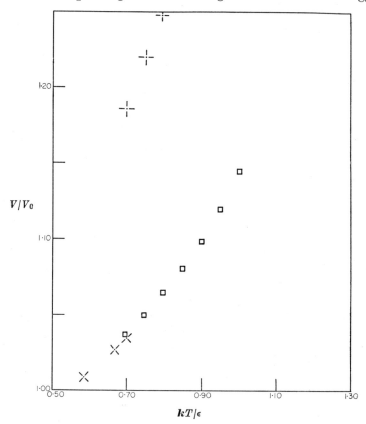

FIG. 4.1. Reduced volumes for 12–6 fluid. Results from L-J-D theory shown thus □, experimental data for liquid argon thus ∹ and for solid argon thus ×.

Not shown in Fig. 4.2 are vapour pressures calculated from the L-J-D theory by assuming that the communal entropy of the condensed phase is Nk, so that the values given by (4.4.10) are divided by ϵ; this was the procedure originally followed by Lennard-Jones and Devonshire.[2] At low temperatures these values are identical with values that would be derived by using the L-J-D theory for both condensed and vapour phases. The latter procedure reduces the entropy of the vapour phase by Nk, which has the same effect on vapour pressures as increasing the entropy of the condensed phase by the same amount. Vapour pressures calculated in this way are not in good agreement with experimental values for either solid or liquid.

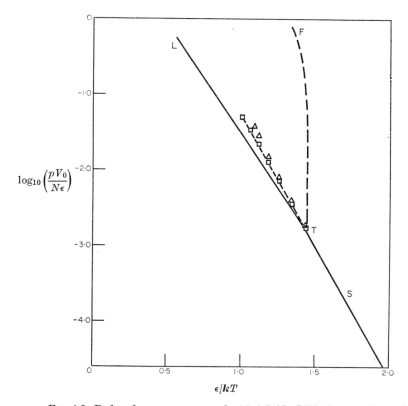

Fig. 4.2. Reduced vapour pressures for 12–6 fluid. LT is the experimental curve for liquid argon, TS the experimental curve for solid argon (extrapolation shown dotted). L-J-D results from equation (4.4.10) shown thus □ and from equations (4.4.11) and (4.4.12) thus △. TF is the solid–liquid equilibrium line.

The comparisons made so far indicate strongly that the condensed phase described by the L-J-D theory is to be identified as a solid and not as a liquid. This view is confirmed by the comparison with results of Monte Carlo calculations for $kT/\epsilon = 2\cdot74$ which has already been made in chapter 2. The L-J-D pressures and energies are in good agreement with the Monte Carlo results on the solid side of the "freezing" transition but not on the compressed gas side (see Figs. 2.6

and 2.7). This comparison is particularly convincing because the
Monte Carlo calculations used the same assumption of additivity of
intermolecular potentials as the L-J-D theory, so that there is no
uncertainty arising from this point. Similar conclusions have already
been drawn from the results of the cell theory as applied to the rigid-
sphere system (section 3.2).

A similar comparison can be made using the extensive measurements
of Michels and his colleagues on compressed gaseous argon. We shall
use the reduced thermodynamic functions derived from the data by
Levelt and listed by Dahler and Hirschfelder.[19] The experimental
results do not extend to such high densities as the Monte Carlo calculations but they have the advantage of providing values of the entropy;
the Monte Carlo calculations give only the pressure and the energy.
Experimental and L-J-D values of pV/NkT and of reduced excess
energy and entropy are compared in Table 4.5.

TABLE 4.5

L-J-D theory compared with properties of compressed gaseous argon

Reduced temperature kT/ϵ	Reduced volume V/V_0	Compression ratio, pV/NkT		Reduced excess energy, $E'/N\epsilon$		Reduced excess entropy, S'/Nk	
		L-J-D	argon	L-J-D	argon	L-J-D	argon
1·3	1·5	0·513	0·853	−4·53	−4·34	−3·14	−2·01
1·3	1·6	0·542	0·621	−4·20	−4·09	−2·92	−1·83
3·0	1·4	2·773	2·749	—	—	—	—
3·0	1·5	2·574	2·380	−3·66	−3·49	−2·71	−1·57
3·0	1·6	2·425	2·112	−3·42	−3·32	−2·54	−1·44

The L-J-D values of pV/NkT and of the energy are not very different
from the experimental values; it is in this region of volume that the
L-J-D curves cross the Monte Carlo curves in Figs. 2.6 and 2.7. However the L-J-D values of the entropy are too low by rather more than
Nk.

In Table 4.6 we compare experimental values of pressure, energy and
entropy for liquid argon at the triple point with values calculated from
the L-J-D theory at the *experimental liquid volume*. The agreement is
unsatisfactory; we must regard the L-J-D theory as describing a
metastable solid expanded by the negative pressure.

TABLE 4.6

*L-J-D theory at experimental liquid volume compared with
liquid argon; $kT/\epsilon = 0.70$*

	Reduced pressure $pV_0/N\epsilon$	Reduced excess energy, $E'/N\epsilon$	Reduced excess entropy, S'/Nk
L-J-D theory	−1·957	−6·46	−4·69
liquid argon	0·000	−5·96	−3·64

The L-J-D theory predicts a critical isotherm at $kT/\epsilon = 1.30$. In Table 4.7 we compare reduced critical constants determined from this isotherm with experimental liquid–gas critical constants for argon. The theoretical and experimental critical temperatures agree fairly closely, but the pressures and volumes show poor agreement. Even if this were not so we should not be justified in identifying the theoretical critical point with the observed liquid gas critical point, for reasons which are discussed in section 4.6.

TABLE 4.7

Critical constants from L-J-D theory and experiment

	L-J-D theory	Experimental, argon
kT_c/ϵ	1·30	1·26
V_c/V_0	1·768	3·16
$p_cV_0/N\epsilon$	0·434	0·116
p_cV_c/RT_c	0·591	0·292

It was proposed by de Boer[20] that the agreement of the L-J-D theory with experiment could be improved by choosing the number of nearest neighbours z smaller than the value 12 corresponding to close-packing. The first difficulty is that regular structures with values of z between 12 and 8 are unknown, so that the relation between density and lattice parameter cannot be determined. De Boer avoided this difficulty by interpolating values of the parameter γ' defined in section 3.2 between the values appropriate for face-centred cubic, body-centred cubic and simple cubic lattices (with $z = 12, 8, 6$, respectively). The meaning of this interpolation is not at all clear. The second difficulty is that the structure with $z = 12$ gives lower calculated free energies than those with smaller values of z, and so should be more stable. If these difficulties are ignored, lower values of z do give volumes closer to the experimental liquid volumes. However, the calculated vapour pressures are much too high, essentially because the theoretical entropy is too low. This procedure cannot be regarded as satisfactory.

4.6   *The Meaning of the L-J-D Theory*

The comparisons in section 4.5 indicate that at least at high densities the L-J-D theory describes a solid. At low densities too the theory restricts the molecular configurations to those in which one molecule occupies each cell; it describes a hypothetical expanded ordered structure, which we may describe briefly as an "expanded solid". This expanded solid is "metastable" with respect to the true gas which has lower free energy. It is also unstable on the molecular level since a whole system of impenetrable barriers would be required to confine the molecules to the cells. However, it is instructive to compare the free energy of the expanded ordered structure, calculated by the L-J-D theory, with the free energy of disordered structures suggested by gas and liquid properties. This comparison is made for the temperature $kT/\epsilon = 1 \cdot 1$ in Fig. 4.3.

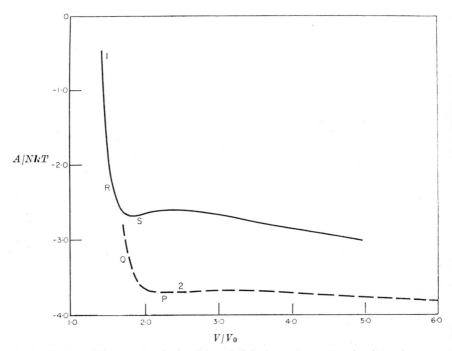

FIG. 4.3. Free energy calculated from L-J-D theory (curve 1) and estimated from properties of liquid and gaseous argon (curve 2); for $kT/\epsilon = 1 \cdot 1$.

The curve 1 refers to the ordered structure; it is calculated from the L-J-D theory. Curve 2 refers to disordered structures. For large values of V/V_0 it is determined from the virial series with the known second and third coefficients for the 12–6 fluid. The behaviour in the neighbourhood of the minimum P is estimated from the vapour pressure and compressibility of liquid argon and the behaviour in the neighbourhood of the point Q is estimated from the freezing pressure and density of liquid argon (assuming that curve 1 describes the solid). The remainder of curve 2 is entirely conjectural.

The apparent phase transition described by the L-J-D theory near its critical temperature corresponds to drawing a common tangent to curve 1 from S to a point somewhat to the right of S. It is a hypothetical transition between a condensed ordered phase and an expanded ordered phase, and it is this transition which disappears at the theoretical critical point. The fact that the theoretical critical point is close to the experimental liquid–gas critical point apparently reflects the fact (which could hardly have been foreseen) that curves 1 and 2 are quite similar, apart from a vertical displacement. In fact of course the whole of curve 1 to the right of R is physically unrealizable since the disordered liquid and gas states are more stable. A common tangent from curve 1 at R to curve 2 at Q describes the solid–liquid equilibrium.

The behaviour to be expected at lower temperatures is shown qualitatively in Fig. 4.4. A common tangent to curve 2 at P and W

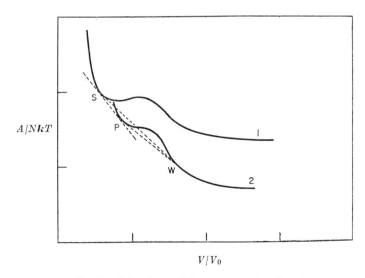

FIG. 4.4. Qualitative behaviour of free energy at a low temperature. Curve 1, ordered structures; curve 2, disordered structures.

corresponds to the liquid–gas equilibrium. Tangents from curve 1 at S to curve 2 at P and W, respectively, correspond to solid–liquid and solid–gas equilibria. The latter is physically unrealizable (above the triple point) because the system finds states of lower free energy by following first the line WP and then PS. However, the line WS corresponds to a point on the extrapolated vapour pressure curve of the solid, as calculated from (4.4.11) and (4.4.12) and plotted in Fig. 4.2. At higher temperatures the "hump" in curve 2 becomes less pronounced and the tangent PW no longer exists, as in Fig. 4.3. This corresponds to the fact that (4.4.11) and (4.4.12) do not have solutions for kT/ϵ greater than 0·924. Thus the extrapolated solid vapour pressure curve comes to an end at $kT/\epsilon = 0·924$; the high temperature solid–gas equilibrium is of course the continuation of the solid–liquid equilibrium corresponding to SP in Fig. 4.4.

REFERENCES

1. LENNARD-JONES, J. E. and DEVONSHIRE, A. F., *Proc. roy. Soc.* 1937, **A163**, 53.
2. LENNARD-JONES, J. E. and DEVONSHIRE, A. F., *Proc. roy. Soc.* 1938, **A165**, 1.
3. LENNARD-JONES, J. E. and DEVONSHIRE, A. F., *Proc. roy. Soc.* 1939, **A169**, 317.
4. LENNARD-JONES, J. E. and DEVONSHIRE, A. F., *Proc. roy. Soc.* 1939, **A170**, 469.
5. DEVONSHIRE, A. F., *Proc. roy. Soc.* 1940, **A174**, 102.
6. CORNER, J. and LENNARD-JONES, J. E., *Proc. roy. Soc.* 1941, **A178**, 401.
7. WENTORF, R. H., JR., BUEHLER, R. J., HIRSCHFELDER, J. O. and CURTISS, C. F., *J. chem. Phys.* 1950, **18**, 1484.
8. FICKETT, W. and WOOD, W. W., *J. chem. Phys.* 1952, **20**, 1624.
9. HILL, T. L., *J. phys. Chem.* 1947, **51**, 1219.
10. PRIGOGINE, I. and GARIKIAN, G., *J. Chim. phys.* 1948, **45**, 273.
11. LENNARD-JONES, J. E. and INGHAM, A. E., *Proc. roy. Soc.* 1925, **A107**, 636.
12. HAMANN, S. D. and DAVID, H. G. To be published.
13. HIRSCHFELDER, J. O., CURTISS, C. F. and BIRD, R. B., *Molecular Theory of Gases and Liquids*, p. 1114 *et seq.*, Chapman & Hall, London, 1954.
14. DOBBS, E. R. and JONES, G. O., *Rep. Progr. Phys.* 1957, **20**, 516.
15. GUGGENHEIM, E. A. and McGLASHAN, M. L., *Proc. roy. Soc.* 1960, **A255**, 456.
16. MICHELS, A., WIJKER, HUB. and WIJKER, HK., *Physica* 1949, **15**, 627.
17. ROWLINSON, J. S., *Liquids and Liquid Mixtures*, Butterworths, London, 1959.
18. CLARK, A. M., DIN, F., ROBB, J., MICHELS, A., WASSENAAR, T. and ZWIETERING, TH., *Physica* 1951, **17**, 876.
19. DAHLER, J. S. and HIRSCHFELDER, J. O., *J. chem. Phys.* 1960, **32**, 330.
20. DE BOER, J., *Proc. roy. Soc.* 1952, **A215**, 4.

CHAPTER 5

THE VARIATIONAL THEORY AND THE CELL MODEL

5.1 *The Variation Principle*

THE intuitive way in which the assumptions of the L-J-D theory are introduced was long regarded as unsatisfactory. In 1950 Kirkwood[1] proposed a variation method based on the cell model which made it possible to determine rigorous upper bounds for the free energy. The method is closely analogous to the Hartree and Hartree–Fock self-consistent field methods of quantum mechanics which are also based on a variation principle. The free energy is expressed in terms of a probability density function describing the probabilities of various molecular configurations. If the correct Boltzmann expression for the probability density function is used then the calculated free energy is equal to the actual free energy of the system. If an approximate expression for the probability density function is used then the calculated free energy must be higher than the actual free energy. Thus if an approximate mathematical form for the probability density function is assumed containing certain arbitrary functions then the optimum approximation of this particular form is found by choosing the arbitrary functions to give the lowest possible value of the calculated free energy. If the assumed approximate form has sufficient flexibility then the calculated minimum free energy should be a good approximation to the actual free energy.

In order to make the calculation feasible Kirkwood proposed that the probability density function should be approximated by a simple product of identical cell distribution functions, each depending on the co-ordinates of one molecule with respect to an origin at the centre of its cell. This corresponds to the assumption of independent motion in the L-J-D theory. However, the method of calculating the free energy is different and leads to different results.

The optimum form for the cell distribution function is the form which gives the lowest calculated free energy. Minimization of the free energy leads to a non-linear integral equation from which the cell distribution function can be calculated. Kirkwood showed that the L-J-D theory

could be regarded in a certain sense as an approximation to a calculation based on this variation method. It seemed likely that the variation
method could be regarded both as a justification for the approximations
of the L-J-D theory and as a method for calculating more accurate
results than those given by the L-J-D theory.

Unfortunately later calculations based on Kirkwood's integral
equation, culminating in the elegant and thorough work of Hirschfelder
and his colleagues,[2,3] have proved that this is not the case. Comparison
with experiment shows that the variational theory based on the cell
model describes solids and not liquids; in this it resembles the L-J-D
theory. However, the variational theory is actually less accurate than
the L-J-D theory. The calculated energies and entropies are lower than
the values calculated from the L-J-D theory, which are already slightly
lower than experimental values for solids and considerably lower than
experimental values for liquids. For the rigid-sphere system the variational theory is much less accurate than the L-J-D theory. For the
12–6 fluid at high densities and low temperatures it is only slightly
less accurate. In this case it can be proved that results calculated from
the variational theory approach the results of the L-J-D theory as the
density is increased and the temperature is lowered (section 5.6). It is
much nearer to the truth to regard the variational theory as justified
insofar as it approximates to the L-J-D theory than to regard the
L-J-D theory as justified by the variational theory.

In fact the variational theory is based on an artificial method of
calculating the free energy, chosen because it has the property that the
calculated free energy is rigorously higher than the actual free energy.
The L-J-D theory is best regarded as an approximation to a direct
evaluation of the configuration integral, which does not have this
property (cf. chapters 6 and 7). There is no prior guarantee that the
variational method will lead to a calculated free energy close to the
actual free energy, since the form chosen for the probability density
function may not have sufficient flexibility to enable it to approximate
closely to the actual function. The calculated results indicate that the
simple product form, which is the only form for which the calculations
can be performed readily, is not sufficiently flexible to give accurate
results.

5.2   *The Integral Equation*

Like the L-J-D theory the variational method considers only configurations with one molecule in each cell. We define a probability

density function $P(\mathbf{r}_1 \ldots \mathbf{r}_N)$ by the statement that the probability that the molecule in cell i (for $i = 1, 2 \ldots N$) is in the volume element $d\mathbf{r}_i$ at $\mathbf{r}_i$, is $P(\mathbf{r}_1 \ldots \mathbf{r}_N) \, d\mathbf{r}_1 \ldots d\mathbf{r}_N$. In fact if Q is the configuration integral and U the potential energy P is given by

$$P(\mathbf{r}_1 \ldots \mathbf{r}_N) = \exp(-U/kT)/Q \tag{5.2.1}$$

The free energy can be calculated either from (2) or from (3)–(5):

$$A^* = -kT \ln Q \tag{5.2.2}$$

$$A^* = E^* - TS^* \tag{5.2.3}$$

$$E^* = \int_{\Delta_1} \ldots \int_{\Delta_N} PU \, d\mathbf{r}_1 \ldots d\mathbf{r}_N \tag{5.2.4}$$

$$S^* = -k \int_{\Delta_1} \ldots \int_{\Delta_N} P \ln P \, d\mathbf{r}_1 \ldots d\mathbf{r}_N \tag{5.2.5}$$

By the notation $\int_{\Delta_1} \ldots \int_{\Delta_N}$ in (4) and (5) we imply that molecule i is to remain in the interior Δ_i of cell i, so that the integrations are to be performed only through the restricted configuration space corresponding to one particular distribution of the molecules in the cells.

If the correct form (1) for P is substituted in (3)–(5) they lead to precisely the same result as (2). If, however, an approximate form for P is substituted in (3)–(5) the calculated free energy is necessarily higher than the correct value given by (2). This is the basis of the variational method. The L-J-D theory is based directly on (2). It should not therefore be surprising if the L-J-D theory gives lower (and possibly more accurate) values of the free energy than can be derived by substituting special approximations for P in (3)–(5).

We now approximate P by a product of identical cell distribution functions:

$$P(\mathbf{r}_1 \ldots \mathbf{r}_N) = \prod_{s=1}^{N} \phi(\mathbf{r}_s - \mathbf{r}_{s0}) \tag{5.2.6}$$

In (6) the vector $\mathbf{r}_{s0}$ specifies the position of the centre of cell s. Substitution of (6) in (3)–(5) leads to the result

$$\frac{A^*}{NkT} = \left(\frac{1}{2kT}\right) \int_{\Delta} \int_{\Delta'} E(\mathbf{r} - \mathbf{r}')\phi(\mathbf{r})\phi(\mathbf{r}') \, d\mathbf{r} \, d\mathbf{r}' + \int_{\Delta} \phi(\mathbf{r}) \ln \phi(\mathbf{r}) \, d\mathbf{r} \tag{5.2.7}$$

$$E(\mathbf{r}) = \sum_l u(|\mathbf{R}_{jl} + \mathbf{r}|) \tag{5.2.8}$$

In (8) $\mathbf{R}_{jl}$ is the vector from the centre of cell j to the centre of cell l, and the summation is to be performed over all cells except j. In deriving (7) we have used the fact that the function $\phi(\mathbf{r})$ is normalized to unity, which follows from (6) and the definition of P as a probability density. Thus we have

$$\int_\Delta \phi(\mathbf{r})\, \mathrm{d}\mathbf{r} = 1 \qquad (5.2.9)$$

The function ϕ which satisfies (9) and gives the lowest free energy is determined by the condition that the change in A^* due to a small variation in ϕ consistent with (9) is zero. This condition leads to a non-linear integral equation for $\phi(\mathbf{r})$, which is most conveniently written in terms of a function $\psi(\mathbf{r})$ analogous to the "cell field" in the L-J-D theory and related to $\phi(\mathbf{r})$ by the equation

$$\phi(\mathbf{r}) = \exp\left[-\psi(\mathbf{r})/kT\right] \Big/ \int_\Delta \exp\left[-\psi(\mathbf{r})/kT\right] \mathrm{d}\mathbf{r} \qquad (5.2.10)$$

In terms of this function the integral equation becomes

$$\psi(\mathbf{r}) = \int_{\Delta'} w(\mathbf{r}-\mathbf{r}')\exp\left[-\psi(\mathbf{r}')/kT\right]\mathrm{d}\mathbf{r}' \Big/ \int_{\Delta'}\exp\left[-\psi(\mathbf{r}')/kT\right]\mathrm{d}\mathbf{r}' \quad (5.2.11)$$

where the function $w(\mathbf{r})$ is defined by (12) and (13):

$$w(\mathbf{r}) = E(\mathbf{r}) - \bar{E} \qquad (5.2.12)$$

$$\bar{E} = \frac{\int_\Delta \int_{\Delta'} E(\mathbf{r}-\mathbf{r}')\exp\left\{-[\psi(\mathbf{r})+\psi(\mathbf{r}')]/kT\right\}\,\mathrm{d}\mathbf{r}\,\mathrm{d}\mathbf{r}'}{\int_\Delta \int_{\Delta'}\exp\left\{-[\psi(\mathbf{r})+\psi(\mathbf{r}')]/kT\right\}\,\mathrm{d}\mathbf{r}\,\mathrm{d}\mathbf{r}'} \qquad (5.2.13)$$

Equation (11) is the integral equation of Kirkwood. It can be solved to determine $\psi(\mathbf{r})$ and therefore $\phi(\mathbf{r})$. If $\psi(\mathbf{r})$ satisfies the integral equation substitution in (3)–(5) shows that the free energy is given by

$$A^*/NkT = \ln v_\mathrm{f} + \bar{E}/2kT \qquad (5.2.14)$$

$$v_\mathrm{f} = \int_\Delta \exp\left[-\psi(\mathbf{r})/kT\right]\mathrm{d}\mathbf{r} \qquad (5.2.15)$$

The free volume v_f defined by (15) is the optimum free volume in the sense of the variational theory.

5.3   *The Relation with the L-J-D Theory*

At least at high densities we expect the function $\phi(\mathbf{r})$ to be sharply peaked in the neighbourhood of the cell centre, and we might expect to obtain an approximate result by replacing $\phi(\mathbf{r})$ by a delta function $\delta(\mathbf{r})$ (i.e. by a function which is zero everywhere except at the origin but infinite at the origin in such a way that (5.2.9) is satisfied). If we regard this as a zero approximation then substitution in (5.2.11)–(5.2.13) leads to a *first* approximation:

$$\psi(\mathbf{r}) = {\sum_l}' \left[u(|\mathbf{R}_{jl} + \mathbf{r}|) - u(|\mathbf{R}_{jl}|) \right] \qquad (5.3.1)$$

$$\bar{E} = {\sum_l}' u(|\mathbf{R}_{jl}|) \qquad (5.3.2)$$

If $\psi(\mathbf{r})$ as given by (1) is replaced by its average over a sphere of radius $|\mathbf{r}|$ ("smearing" approximation) then substitution in (5.2.14) and (5.2.15) leads to results identical with the L-J-D theory. In this sense the L-J-D theory can be regarded as an approximation to the variational theory.

In fact the L-J-D theory gives values of the free energy lower than the optimum values determined from (5.2.11)–(5.2.15). This does not contradict the assertion that solutions of equation (5.2.11) minimize the expression (5.2.7) for the free energy. The L-J-D theory results when (1) and (2) are substituted in (5.2.14) and (5.2.15); but the latter equations are equivalent to (5.2.7) only when $\psi(\mathbf{r})$ satisfies the integral equation (5.2.11).[4]

5.4   *Solution of the Integral Equation for Rigid Spheres*

Wood[5] pointed out that the integral equation (5.2.11) can be solved exactly in a very simple form for the case of rigid spherical molecules. A face-centred cubic lattice of cells is assumed, so that the cell Δ is a dodecahedron of altitude $a/2$, where a is the distance between the centres of neighbouring cells. Then (5.2.11) is satisfied exactly if we assume

$$\psi(\mathbf{r}) = 0, \qquad \mathbf{r} \text{ in } \Delta^*$$

$$= \infty, \qquad \mathbf{r} \text{ not in } \Delta^* \qquad (5.4.1)$$

where Δ^* is a dodecahedron similar to Δ but with altitude $(a - D)/2$, where D is the rigid sphere diameter. The free volume is equal to the volume of the dodecahedron Δ^*, given by

$$v_{\mathrm{f}} = (V^{1/3} - V_0^{1/3})^3/N \qquad (5.4.2)$$

where V_0 is $ND^3/\sqrt{2}$. The free energy and pressure are given by

$$A^* = -3NkT \ln \left[(V/N)^{1/3} - (V_0/N)^{1/3} \right] \qquad (5.4.3)$$

$$p = (NkT/V)/[1 - (V_0/V)^{1/3}] \qquad (5.4.4)$$

Pressures calculated from (4) are plotted in Fig. 2.5 where they are compared with Monte Carlo results. They are a little lower than the Monte Carlo "solid" values, but approach the latter values at high densities. Equation (4) is identical with equation (3.2.10) based on the simple cell theory with the smearing approximation, which is the equivalent for rigid spherical molecules of the L-J-D theory. However, the free energy calculated from (3) is higher than that calculated from the simple theory (equation (3.2.7)) by the amount $NkT \ln (4\pi\sqrt{2}/3)$, or $1.78 \, NkT$. Correspondingly the entropy is lower by $1.78 \, Nk$. It is almost certain that the free energy given by (3.2.7) is itself too high (cf. chapter 7), so that the free energy given by (3) is much too high.

The reason for this can be understood in very simple terms. The integral equation (5.2.11) applied to rigid spheres implies that a given molecule excludes other molecules not just from those regions lying within distance D of its instantaneous position, but from all regions within distance D of any point in its own free volume Δ^*. That is the molecule is regarded as excluding all the time all the regions that it can exclude as it moves through its free volume. This leads to an estimate of the free volume which is much too small. The L-J-D theory regards the molecule as excluding all the time those regions which it actually excludes in a *typical* position (at the cell centre). This is a much better approximation.

Wood remarks that the low free energy given by (3.2.7) is due to an inconsistency in that it does not correspond to any real cell distribution function $\phi(\mathbf{r})$ (cf. section 5.3). This is an inconsistency only within the framework of the variational theory. The real justification for (3.2.7) lies in (5.2.2) rather than (5.2.7).

5.5 *Realistic Potential Functions*

Dahler and Hirschfelder[3] have solved the integral equation (5.2.11) for a wide range of temperatures and densities for molecules interacting according to the 12–6 potential. Earlier calculations of Mayer and Careri[6,7] and Levine et al.[8] were less extensive and used a Gaussian approximation for the function $\phi(\mathbf{r})$ and a Morse function potential approximating to the 12–6 potential. We shall base our comparisons with experiment on the work of Dahler and Hirschfelder.

Apart from the fundamental assumptions of the variational theory the calculations of Hirschfelder and Dahler involved two further approximations. The cell distribution function $\phi(\mathbf{r})$ was approximated by a spherically symmetrical function depending only on the distance from the cell centre; and the interactions between non-nearest neighbours were approximated by the values appropriate for molecules at their cell centres. The first of these approximations corresponds to the "smearing" approximation in the L-J-D theory. The second implies that the tendency of second and further neighbours to draw the enclosed molecule towards the boundary of its cell is neglected. The effect of this is that the calculated entropy, and to a lesser extent the calculated energy, are too low. The errors due to the latter approximation are probably comparable with the corresponding differences between "one-shell" and "three-shell" free volumes in the L-J-D theory. On this basis one would expect the calculated entropy to be too low by less than about 0.4 Nk in the neighbourhood of the triple point.[9]

Dahler and Hirschfelder corrected their results to allow for the presence of an equilibrium number of holes or vacant cells, using a method due to Levine et al.[8] The corrections are entirely negligible at a density corresponding to that of solid argon at the triple point, and are small at all liquid densities. Calculations were made for simple cubic, body-centred cubic, face-centred cubic and hexagonal close-packed lattice structures. The last two structures gave identical results with calculated free energies considerably lower at all densities than those calculated for body-centred or simple cubic structures. Thus the stable structure should be either cubic or hexagonal close-packed, and we shall use the values corresponding to these lattices in our comparisons.

In Table 5.1 we compare properties of the condensed phase at zero pressure interpolated from the tables of Dahler and Hirschfelder with experimental data for solid and liquid argon at the triple point. Values given by the L-J-D theory are also included for comparison.

TABLE 5.1

Calculated zero pressure properties at $kT/\epsilon = 0.7$ compared with experimental data

	Reduced volume, V/V_0	Reduced excess energy, $E'/N\epsilon$	Reduced excess entropy, S'/Nk
Dahler and Hirschfelder	1·018	−7·46	−5·98
L-J-D	1·037	−7·32	−5·51
Solid argon	1·035	−7·14	−5·33
Liquid argon	1·186	−5·96	−3·64

The values derived from the variational theory are close to those derived from the L-J-D theory and to the experimental values for

F

solid argon. The major discrepancy is in the entropy, which is appreciably too low. Correct allowance for the effect of further neighbours on the free volume would raise the calculated entropy, though it would probably still lie a little below the L-J-D value. Neither theory gives results close to the experimental data for liquid argon. A comparison of calculated and experimental data at the experimental liquid volume for argon is shown in Table 5.2. Both the variational and L-J-D theories gives pressures, energies and entropies considerably lower than the experimental values for liquid argon. This table shows that the corrections due to the presence of holes are negligible at liquid densities.

TABLE 5.2

Calculated and experimental properties at experimental liquid volume
$$(V/V_0 = 1{\cdot}186,\ kT/\epsilon = 0{\cdot}70)$$

	Reduced pressure $pV_0/N\epsilon$	Reduced excess energy, $E'/N\epsilon$	Reduced excess entropy, S'/Nk
Dahler and Hirschfelder (no holes)	−2·763	−6·521	−5·222
Dahler and Hirschfelder (holes)	−2·747	−6·519	−5·219
L-J-D	−1·96	−6·46	−4·69
Liquid argon	0·00	−5·96	−3·64

The differences between the variational theory and the L-J-D theory become larger at higher temperatures. This is shown in Figs. 2.6 and 2.7 which compare values of pV/NkT and $E'/N\epsilon$. The difference between the values of $E'/N\epsilon$ given by the variational theory and the L-J-D theory is about three times as large at $V/V_0 = 1{\cdot}0$, $kT/\epsilon = 2{\cdot}74$ as at $V/V_0 = 1{\cdot}0$, $kT/\epsilon = 0{\cdot}7$. The L-J-D pressures and energies are close to but a little below the Monte Carlo "solid" results, while the results of Dahler and Hirschfelder are definitely too low if, as seems likely, the Monte Carlo results are substantially correct. The fact that the errors of the variational theory and the differences from the L-J-D theory increase as the temperature is raised is consistent with the results for the rigid-sphere system (section 5.4).

5.6   *Discussion*

The comparisons given above show clearly that the variational free volume theory must be considered as a theory of solids rather than liquids. Considered as a classical theory of solids it is apparently slightly less accurate than the L-J-D theory for 12–6 molecules at

$kT/\epsilon = 0.7$ and appreciably less accurate at $kT/\epsilon = 2.74$. For rigid spherical molecules, which we may regard approximately as a limiting case for infinite temperature, it is much less accurate than the L-J-D theory. The argument of section 5.3 shows that the L-J-D theory may be regarded as the first approximation in an iterative solution of Kirkwood's equation, the zero approximation being the δ-function distribution. However, for rigid spherical molecules this iterative procedure is not convergent but oscillatory.[5] Thus the argument of section 5.3 does not explain the relation between the two theories completely.

In fact we shall prove that the two theories are *asymptotically equivalent* for a system in which the forces may be regarded as harmonic and the displacements as small—that is for a harmonic oscillator model with high frequency. For any continuous and differentiable potential function this model becomes appropriate at low temperatures and sufficiently high densities. However, for rigid spheres this model is never appropriate, and the variational theory gives values of the free volume which are much too small even at the highest densities.

We assume that the cell distribution function $\phi(\mathbf{r})$ has the normalized Gaussian form (1), which must be asymptotically valid[3] at low temperatures and high densities if the potential function is differentiable:

$$\phi(x, y, z) = \left(\frac{\gamma}{\pi}\right)^{3/2} \exp\left[-\gamma(x^2 + y^2 + z^2)\right] \tag{5.6.1}$$

To evaluate the integrals in (5.2.7) we choose the x direction to coincide with that of the vector $\mathbf{R}_{jl}$ and expand $u(|\mathbf{R}_{jl} + \mathbf{r} - \mathbf{r}'|)$ in powers of x, x', etc., with the results

$$u(|\mathbf{R}_{jl} + \mathbf{r} - \mathbf{r}'|) = u(R_{jl}) + (x - x')u'(R_{jl}) + u'(R_{jl}) \times$$
$$\times [(y - y')^2 + (z - z')^2]/2R_{jl} + \tfrac{1}{2}u''(R_{jl})(x - x')^2 + O(x^3) \tag{5.6.2}$$

$$\int \phi(\mathbf{r})\phi(\mathbf{r}')u(|\mathbf{R}_{jl} + \mathbf{r} - \mathbf{r}'|)\,d\mathbf{r}\,d\mathbf{r}'$$

$$= u(R_{jl}) + \frac{1}{2\gamma}[u''(R_{jl}) + 2R_{jl}^{-1}u'(R_{jl})] + O\left(\frac{1}{\gamma^2}\right) \tag{5.6.3}$$

$$\int \phi(\mathbf{r}) \ln \phi(\mathbf{r})\,d\mathbf{r} = \tfrac{3}{2}\ln\left(\frac{\gamma}{\pi}\right) - \tfrac{3}{2} \tag{5.6.4}$$

If these results are substituted in (5.2.7) the free energy is found to be given by

$$\frac{A^*}{NkT} = \frac{1}{2kT}\sum_l u(R_{jl}) + \frac{1}{4\gamma kT}\sum_l [u''(R_{jl}) + 2R_{jl}^{-1}u'(R_{jl})]$$

$$+ \tfrac{3}{2}\ln\left(\frac{\gamma}{\pi}\right) - \tfrac{3}{2} + O\left(\frac{1}{\gamma^2}\right) \tag{5.6.5}$$

The value of γ which minimizes this expression can be found by equating the derivative to zero, which gives

$$\gamma = \frac{1}{6kT} \sum_{l} [u''(R_{jl}) + 2R_{jl}^{-1}u'(R_{jl})] + O\left(\frac{1}{\gamma}\right) \qquad (5.6.6)$$

Substituting this in (5.6.5) gives the optimum free energy:

$$\frac{A^*}{NkT} = \frac{1}{2kT} \sum_{l} u(R_{jl}) + \tfrac{3}{2}\ln\left(\frac{\gamma}{\pi}\right) + O\left(\frac{1}{\gamma}\right) \qquad (5.6.7)$$

Apart from the terms of order $1/\gamma$ this is exactly the result given by the L-J-D theory. If in equation (2) we set $x' = y' = z' = 0$ and average with respect to x, y, z over the surface of a sphere of radius r we find (since the average $\langle x^2 \rangle$ of x^2 is $\tfrac{1}{3}r^2$) the result

$$\langle u(|\mathbf{R}_{jl} + \mathbf{r}|)\rangle = u(R_{jl}) + \tfrac{1}{6}[u''(R_{jl}) + 2R_{jl}^{-1}u'(R_{jl})]r^2 + O(r^3) \qquad (5.6.8)$$

From this it follows that the cell field in the L-J-D theory is given by

$$[\psi(\mathbf{r}) - \psi(0)]/kT = \gamma r^2 + O(r^3) \qquad (5.6.9)$$

with γ defined by (6). Thus the free volume in the L-J-D theory is $(\pi/\gamma)^{3/2}$, so that the free energy is given by (7).

This result is quite different from that of section 5.3. In section 5.3 we showed that the L-J-D theory could be regarded as the first approximation in an iterative solution of Kirkwood's integral equation. Here we have shown that the L-J-D theory and the exact solution of Kirkwood's equation are asymptotically equivalent at high densities and low temperatures. Since the variational theory appears to be less accurate than the L-J-D theory at high temperatures and low densities for the 12–6 potential and at all densities for the hard-sphere system, it seems that the partial success of the variational theory is to be ascribed to this asymptotic equivalence to the L-J-D theory.

REFERENCES

1. KIRKWOOD, J. G., *J. chem. Phys.* 1950, **18**, 380.
2. DAHLER, J. S., HIRSCHFELDER, J. O. and THACHER, H. C., *J. chem. Phys.* 1956, **25**, 249.
3. DAHLER, J. S. and HIRSCHFELDER, J. O., *J. chem. Phys.* 1960, **32**, 330.
4. BARKER, J. A., *Proc. roy. Soc.* 1955, A230, 390.
5. WOOD, W. W., *J. chem. Phys.* 1952, **20**, 1334.
6. MAYER, J. E. and CARERI, G., *J. chem. Phys.* 1952, **20**, 1001.
7. CARERI, G., *J. chem. Phys.* 1952, **20**, 1114.
8. LEVINE, S., MAYER, J. E. and AROESTE, H., *J. chem. Phys.* 1957, **26**, 201.
9. WENTORF, R. H., JR., BUEHLER, R. J., HIRSCHFELDER, J. O. and CURTISS, C. F., *J. chem. Phys.* 1950, **18**, 1484.

CHAPTER 6

A DETAILED CELL THEORY

6.1 *The Assumptions of the L-J-D Theory*

We now undertake a detailed analysis of the assumptions and approximations of the L-J-D theory, in order to determine whether this theory can be improved in such a way as to make it capable of describing the liquid state as well as the solid state. There are three points to be examined — the assumption that each cell contains one molecule, the assumption that the molecules move independently in their cells, and the validity of the smearing approximation.

We shall find that the error due to the smearing approximation is not serious at high densities and can be corrected comparatively easily at lower densities. Satisfactory methods have also been developed for taking into account the correlated motions of the molecules which are neglected by the assumption of independent motions. The remaining assumption, that each cell contains one molecule, is more fundamental and more difficult to improve. Approximate methods for taking into account multiple occupation of cells have been developed, and are probably adequate at densities not much higher than the critical density. However, most calculations have indicated that the effects of double occupation of cells are entirely negligible at densities as high as the density of the liquid at the triple point. We shall present evidence based on comparison with experiment that this is probably not the case, and we shall indicate the probable reasons for the fact that theoretical calculations have underestimated the importance of double occupation of cells at high densities.

The basis for discussion is provided by an analysis of the configuration integral due to Kirkwood.[1] Kirkwood showed that if the available volume V is divided into an arbitrary lattice of N cells then the configuration integral is given by

$$Q = \frac{1}{N!} \sum_{\substack{m_1...m_N \\ \Sigma m_s = N}} Q^{(m_1...m_N)} \left(\frac{N!}{\prod m_s!} \right) \tag{6.1.1}$$

In this equation $Q^{(m_1 \ldots m_N)}$ is a restricted configuration integral defined as the integral of $e^{-U/kT}$ over that part of the total configuration space for which m_1 particular molecules lie in cell 1, m_2 particular molecules in cell 2, and so on. Since the number of ways of allocating the molecules to cells so that there are m_s molecules in cell s is $(N \, ! \, / \prod m_s!)$, equation (1) is an identity. The effect of this identity is to *classify* the possible configurations according to the numbers of molecules in the various cells, and to express the total configuration integral as a *sum* of restricted integrals corresponding to the various modes of occupation of the cells. In discussing the L-J-D theory we neglected all terms in (1) except $Q^{(1 \ldots 1)}$. Of course (1) is of purely formal interest unless we can evaluate the integrals $Q^{(m_1 \ldots m_N)}$; we shall return to this point in section 6.4.

Since we expect intuitively that the term $Q^{(1 \ldots 1)}$ is the most important term in (1), we may define a parameter β by the equation

$$\beta^N Q^{(1 \ldots 1)} = \sum_{\substack{m_1 \ldots m_N \\ \Sigma m_s = N}} \frac{Q^{(m_1 \ldots m_N)}}{\prod m_s !} \tag{6.1.2}$$

The configurational free energy is then given *exactly* though formally by

$$A^* = - N kT \ln Q^{(1 \ldots 1)} - N kT \ln \beta \tag{6.1.3}$$

The second term in (3) is referred to as the "communal free energy", while the "communal entropy" is given by

$$S_{\text{comm}} = N k(\ln \beta + T \, \partial \ln \beta / \partial T) \tag{6.1.4}$$

If β were independent of temperature the communal entropy would be $N k \ln \beta$. At low densities, in the perfect gas limit, β is equal to e. At *solid* densities β is very close to 1. The value of β at intermediate densities is discussed in section 6.4.

We now describe a procedure[2-4] by which $Q^{(1 \ldots 1)}$ can in principle be evaluated with any desired accuracy. The procedure involves a sequence of approximations, of which the first corresponds to the L-J-D theory with its neglect of all correlations between the motions of different molecules, while higher approximations take into account successively correlations between the motions of two, three and more molecules. The corrections due to binary correlations (that is correlations between the motions of two molecules) have been evaluated explicitly for the 12-6 potential (see section 6.3). The fact that these corrections are comparatively small is the fundamental justification for the L-J-D theory as an approximate classical theory of solids. In fact allowance for the binary correlation effects improves the agreement between the predictions of the L-J-D theory and the experimental properties of solid argon, and if corrections for quantum effects are also made this agreement is even closer (chapter 11). The status of the L-J-D theory as a theory of *liquids* depends of course on the value of β, since it seems that β cannot be assumed to be close to 1 at liquid densities.

The potential energy is given by

$$U = \frac{1}{2} \sum_{i,j} u(R_{ij}) \qquad (6.1.5)$$

The subscripts i, j identify either a cell or the molecule in that cell. The factor $\frac{1}{2}$ appears since the summation is taken for unrestricted i and j, so that each pair interaction occurs twice. If we denote by R_{ij0} the distance between cell centre j and molecule i, and by R_{i0j0} the distance between cell centres i and j, then we may write the *identity*

$$u(R_{ij}) = u(R_{i0j0}) + [u(R_{ij0}) - u(R_{i0j0})] + [u(R_{i0j}) - u(R_{i0j0})] + \Delta_{ij}$$

$$(6.1.6)$$

$$\Delta_{ij} = u(R_{ij}) - u(R_{ij0}) - u(R_{i0j}) + u(R_{i0j0}) \qquad (6.1.7)$$

Substituting (6) in (5) we find

$$U = \frac{1}{2} \sum_{i,j} u(R_{i0j0}) + \sum_i \sum_j [u(R_{ij0}) - u(R_{i0j0})] + \frac{1}{2} \sum_{i,j} \Delta_{ij} \quad (6.1.8)$$

The sum over j in the second term is the change of potential energy when molecule i moves from its cell centre to its actual position, with all other molecules remaining at their cell centres. Thus it is just the (unsmeared) "cell field" of the L-J-D theory. Similarly the first term in (8) is the "lattice energy" U_0. Thus we have established the identity

$$U = U_0 + \sum_i [\psi(\mathbf{r}_i) - \psi(0)] + \frac{1}{2} \sum_{i,j} \Delta_{ij} \qquad (6.1.9)$$

with Δ_{ij} defined by (7).

In words what we have done is to recognize that the L-J-D theory arises if the potential energy of two molecules i and j is approximated by the energy when the molecules are at their cell centres, augmented by the changes of energy arising when each molecule moves to its actual position with the other remaining at its cell centre. The correction required to make this approximate value equal to the true potential energy is just Δ_{ij}, defined by (7).

If the last term in (9) is neglected the motions of the molecules may be regarded as independent, but the terms Δ_{ij} give rise to correlations between the motions of different molecules.

We define a quantity f_{ij} by the relation

$$f_{ij} = \exp\left(-\Delta_{ij}/kT\right) - 1 \tag{6.1.10}$$

As a consequence of (9) the restricted configuration integral $Q^{(1...1)}$ assumes the form

$$Q^{(1...1)} = \exp\left(-U_0/kT\right) \int_{\text{cell}} \cdots \int_{\text{cell}} \prod_i \exp\left\{-[\psi(\mathbf{r}_i) - \psi(0)]/kT\right\} \times$$
$$\times \prod_{j>k} (1 + f_{jk})\, d\mathbf{r}_1 \ldots d\mathbf{r}_N \tag{6.1.11}$$

This expression can be evaluated by methods analogous to those used in the theory of imperfect gases. If the product of factors $(1 + f_{jk})$ is expanded the integration over the co-ordinates of all molecules not involved in the factors f_{jk} in a given term may be performed immediately, with the result

$$Q^{(1...1)} = v_f^N \exp\left(-U_0/kT\right)[1 + \sum \langle f_{ij}\rangle + \sum \langle f_{ij}f_{kl}\rangle + \ldots] \tag{6.1.12}$$

In (12) the angular brackets $\langle\ \rangle$ imply averaging according to the equation

$$\langle f_{ij} \ldots f_{kl}\rangle = \int \cdots \int \prod{}'(\exp\left\{-[\psi(\mathbf{r}_i) - \psi(0)]/kT\right\}/v_f)f_{ij} \ldots f_{kl}\, d\mathbf{r}_i \ldots d\mathbf{r}_l$$
$$\tag{6.1.13}$$

In the product $\prod'$ appearing in (13) there is one factor for each molecule whose number appears as a subscript in the product $f_{ij} \ldots f_{kl}$.

Using the result (12) it is in principle possible to evaluate $Q^{(1...1)}$ with any desired accuracy. In practice of course the integrations required to evaluate $\langle f_{ij} \ldots f_{kl}\rangle$ increase rapidly in complexity, and only the simplest term, namely $\langle f_{ij}\rangle$, has been evaluated (except for the case of harmonic forces). We shall return to this point in section 6.3, after considering the smearing approximation.

6.2   The Smearing Approximation

The accuracy of the smearing approximation for rigid spherical molecules on a face-centred cubic lattice was examined by Buehler et al.[5] They evaluated the correct free volume, which in this case is the volume of the region of complicated shape bounded by spheres of diameter D centred at neighbouring lattice sites. For V/ND^3 greater than 2, part of the boundary is formed by the planes bounding the dodecahedral cell. Some typical results are shown in Table 6.1.

TABLE 6.1

Free volume for rigid spheres on face-centred cubic lattice

V/ND^3	Correct values		Values found with smearing approximation	
	v_f/D^3	pV/NkT	v_f/D^3	pV/NkT
0·8779	0·0025	14	0·0018	14·4
1·1854	0·0407	6·5	0·0275	6·3
2·0000	0·4912	3·8	0·2977	3·4

The correct free volumes are larger than the values found with the smearing approximation by an almost constant factor of about 1.5. Thus the pressures calculated from the "smeared" free volumes are not very different from those calculated from the correct free volumes, but values of the entropy derived from the smeared free volumes would be too low by about $0·6Nk$. There is no tendency for the smearing approximation to become accurate at high densities. In this respect the rigid-sphere system is a special case. The errors of the smearing approximation arise from the fact that we average the potential energy over the surface of a sphere and then form $\exp(-U_{av}/kT)$, rather than averaging $\exp(-U/kT)$ itself. We should expect that this procedure would be least satisfactory when the potential energy has large positive values in restricted regions. In fact for rigid spheres $\exp(-U_{av}/kT)$ becomes zero as soon as the sphere over which we average *touches* the exclusion spheres of neighbouring molecules.

For more realistic (i.e. differentiable) potential functions the potential energy can be expanded in a power series in the co-ordinates of the molecule with respect to the cell centre. At reasonably high densities and low temperatures the free volume is determined primarily by the quadratic terms in this series — that is a harmonic oscillator model becomes appropriate (cf. section 5.6). It is a consequence of the symmetry of the lattice that the coefficients of x^2, y^2 and z^2 in the series are *equal*, so that the change in potential energy is proportional to ρ^2, where ρ is the distance from the cell centre. Thus the exact and smeared cell fields are *identical* as far as the quadratic terms are concerned. As a result of this the error due to the smearing approximation tends to zero as the density increases.

This is illustrated by the results for the 12–6 potential shown in Table 6.2. These results were derived by Barker[3] by straightforward numerical integration based on equation (4.2.5).

TABLE 6.2

Ratio of correct free volume to smeared free volume;
12–6 potential, $kT/\epsilon = 1.2$

V/V_0	2·0	2·4	2·8	3·2	3·6	4·0
v_f(correct)/v_f(smeared)	1·15	1·29	1·35	1·41	1·42	1·35

The error due to the smearing approximation passes through a maximum in the neighbourhood of the critical density ($V/V_0 \simeq 3\cdot2$), and is already small when V/V_0 is as small as 2. It seems certain that the error would be negligible at the density of the liquid in the neighbourhood of the triple point, and *a fortiori* at the density of the solid.

6.3 *The Correlation Effect*

We now resume consideration of the effects of the correlated motions of the molecules, using equation (6.1.12). We shall assume that the factors f_{ij} can be neglected unless the molecules i and j occupy a nearest-neighbour pair of cells. Calculations have shown[3] that this approximation is valid at densities near the critical density, and it probably does not lead to serious error at higher densities. If we assume further that the averages of products of factors $\langle f_{ij} \dots f_{kl} \rangle$ can be approximated by products of averages $\langle f_{ij} \rangle \dots \langle f_{kl} \rangle$ then (6.1.12) becomes

$$Q^{(1\dots1)} = v_f^N \exp\left(-U_0/kT\right)(1+f)^{\frac{1}{2}zN} \tag{6.3.1}$$

$$f = \langle f_{ij} \rangle \tag{6.3.2}$$

In (1) z denotes the coordination number of the lattice. The number of terms in the summation in (6.1.12) involving a product of r factors f_{ij} is equal to the number of ways of selecting r factors out of the total number $\frac{1}{2}zN$; this is the binomial coefficient $\binom{\frac{1}{2}zN}{r}$. Since each such term contributes f^r to the sum, the result (1) follows immediately.

The assumption that the average of a product $f_{ij} \dots f_{kl}$ can be replaced by the product of averages is exactly true if the product $f_{ij} \dots f_{kl}$ involves each subscript once only, that is if there is no repeated subscript. However, the replacement of $\langle f_{ij}f_{jk} \rangle$ by $\langle f_{ij} \rangle \langle f_{jk} \rangle$ involves an approximation. Thus while (1) takes account correctly of correlated motions involving two molecules (binary correlations) it neglects correlated motions involving three or more molecules (ternary and higher correlations). We shall find that allowance for binary correlations by the use of equation (1) corrects the major part (75 – 85 per cent for a harmonic force model) of the error due to the assumption of independent motions, which error is itself comparatively small.

In the theory of solids these correlation effects are customarily taken into account in an entirely different way. If the forces are harmonic, i.e. if only terms quadratic in the coordinates of the molecules occur in the potential energy, then the partition function for the crystal may be expressed as a product of partition functions for the normal modes of vibration. The Einstein model assumes that all the normal modes have the same frequency, corresponding to the vibration of an atom with its neighbours fixed. In fact there is a whole spectrum of vibration frequencies ranging from a maximum frequency down to zero. At very low temperatures, because of the quantization of the vibrations, only the lowest frequencies are important. In these low frequency vibrations the molecules move almost in phase over distances large compared with their spacing; hence the usefulness of the Debye model. We are concerned with high temperatures at which classical statistical mechanics becomes applicable. In these conditions the frequencies close to the frequency at which a molecule vibrates when its neighbours are fixed are most important. The differences of these frequencies from the frequency with the neighbours fixed are determined by short-range correlations. The correlation corrections Δ_{ij} correspond exactly to the off-diagonal terms in the frequency matrix which produce the differences from the frequency corresponding to the case of fixed neighbours.

In Table 6.3 we compare values of the classical "correlation free energy" for a simple harmonic force model calculated[6] by different methods. The correlation free energy A_{corr} is defined as the difference between the true free energy of the system and the free energy calculated using the assumption of independent motion. It is thus a measure of the error caused by the latter assumption. The model considered is a face-centred cubic lattice in which the nearest-neighbour interactions are derived from the 12–6 potential by retaining only quadratic terms, and interactions between non-nearest neighbours are neglected. The "exact" values were calculated using a method based on the Born–Kármán lattice dynamics[7] and developed by Salter,[8] while the "binary correlation" and "binary + ternary correlation" values are derived from equation (6.1.12) including, respectively, binary and binary and ternary correlation terms. For the case of harmonic forces A_{corr}/NkT is independent of temperature, so that the correlation corrections increase the entropy but do not affect the energy. This remains true to a very good approximation at high densities when anharmonic terms are included.

TABLE 6.3

"Correlation free energy", face-centred cubic lattice, nearest-neighbour harmonic 12–6 interactions

	V/V_0			
	1·0	1·1	1·2	1·3
A_{corr}/NkT, exact values (lattice dynamics)	−0·23	−0·19	−0·14	−0·09
A_{corr}/NkT, binary correlation	−0·19	−0·16	−0·12	−0·07
A_{corr}/NkT, binary + ternary correlation	−0·24	−0·19	−0·13	—0·07

It is apparent that allowance for binary correlations corrects about 75–85 per cent of the error due to the assumption of independent motion, while allowance for ternary correlations corrects most of the remaining error. The advantage of the method based on equation (6.1.12) is of course that it is in no way restricted to the case of harmonic forces.

The evaluation of the integral defining $\langle f_{ij} \rangle$ is a matter of considerable difficulty when the forces are not harmonic. The simplest method would be to expand $\exp(-\Delta_{ij}/kT)$ in powers of the co-ordinates of the two molecules i and j and integrate the resulting series. Unfortunately the convergence of this procedure is unsatisfactory for practical use, and more complicated methods must be used. Two approximate methods have been developed by Barker. The first[3] is appropriate for comparatively low densities; we shall discuss the results for densities in the region of the critical density in section 6.4. The second method,[6] based on the use of an analytical approximation to the cell field, is appropriate for high densities. The values in Table 6.4 have been calculated using this method with the help of electronic computing facilities. Most of the hand-calculated values given in the original publication by Barker[6] agree within about 1 per cent with the values in Table 6.4. However, one value (for $kT/\epsilon = 0·75$, $V/V_0 = 1·4$) is too high by about 5 per cent, presumably as the result of a computational error. This error led to distortion in the calculated free energy curves and the erroneous conclusion that the free energy against volume curve when corrected for correlation effects showed a concave region indicating the existence of a second condensed phase. With the more accurate values in Table 6.4 this conclusion cannot be maintained. Apparently the "communal" free energy, arising from multiple occupation of cells, is essential for the existence of the liquid state.

TABLE 6.4

Values of $(1 + f)$ *for the 12–6 potential*

$V/V_0 =$ kT/ϵ	1·0	1·1	1·2	1·3	1·4	1·5	1·6
0·75	$1·03_4$	$1·04_3$	$1·04_9$	$1·05_1$	$1·04_2$	$1·03_5$	$1·02_6$
0·90	$1·03_5$	$1·04_3$	$1·04_9$	$1·05_0$	$1·04_1$	$1·03_6$	$1·02_4$

The results in Table 6.4 show that $1 + f$ is effectively independent of temperature in the range of densities and temperatures considered, so that the effect of the correlation correction is to increase the entropy without affecting the energy. For *solid* argon at the triple point the increase in entropy would be about $0·2 \, Nk$, of the same order as the difference between the theoretical and experimental values in Table 4.4. There is also a slight increase in the zero-pressure volume.

In Table 6·5 we compare values of pressure, energy and entropy calculated from the L-J-D theory corrected for correlation effects with the properties of liquid argon at the triple point. The theoretical values were calculated using the experimental liquid volume (cf. Table 4.6) and the correlation corrections were made using the results in Table 6.4. The conclusions to be drawn from Table 6.5 are not seriously modified when quantum corrections are made (see chapter 11).

TABLE 6.5

L-J-D theory with correlation corrections (using experimental liquid volume) compared with liquid argon at triple point

	Reduced pressure, $pV_0/N\epsilon$	Reduced excess energy, $E'/N\epsilon$	Reduced excess entropy, S'/Nk
L-J-D with correlations	−1·79	−6·46	−4·41
liquid argon	0·00	−5·96	−3.64

From the results in Table 6.4 it appears that the calculated entropy is too low by about $0.8\ Nk$, while the calculated energy is too low by $0.5\ N\epsilon$, which is close to $0.7\ Nk$ (since kT/ϵ is 0.7). Combining these results we see that the calculated free energy is only about $0.1\ NkT$ above the experimental value, though if quantum corrections are made the calculated free energy becomes a little higher. On the other hand the discrepancy in the pressure remains large. These facts could be understood if the communal parameter β of section 6.1 were greater than 1 by an amount which is small at the liquid density, perhaps about 0.2 to 0.3, but which increases rapidly with increasing volume (to explain the discrepancy in pressure) and with increasing temperature (to explain the discrepancies in entropy and energy). If in addition β were effectively equal to 1 at the solid density we should be in a position to understand the existence of two condensed phases. We shall discuss these questions further in section 6.4.

6.4   *Multiple Occupation of Cells*

We now move from problems which can be regarded as solved, at least in principle, to the central unsolved problem of the cell theory. This is the problem of the "communal free energy", due to double or multiple occupation of cells. Although the methods which have been developed for dealing with this problem are probably adequate at low densities they are probably *not* adequate at high densities.

To evaluate the effects of multiple occupation we return to the formal classification of configurations provided by equation (6.1.2). To find explicit results it is of course necessary to evaluate the restricted phase integrals $Q^{(m_1 \ldots m_N)}$ for cases where $m_1 \ldots m_N$ are not all equal to 1. Pople[9] and Janssens and Prigogine[10] proposed an approximate method for doing this based on the idea that each multiply occupied cell would change the value of the restricted configuration integral by a constant factor, depending only on the number of molecules in the cell. Thus the restricted configuration integral would be multiplied by a factor ω_2 for each doubly occupied cell, by a factor ω_3 for each trebly occupied cell, and so on:

$$Q^{(m_1 \ldots m_N)} = \left(\prod_s \omega_{m_s}\right).Q^{(1 \ldots 1)}$$

$$= \left(\prod_j \omega_j^{n_j}\right).Q^{(1 \ldots 1)} \qquad (6.4.1)$$

In the second form of (1) n_j is the number of cells containing j molecules in the arrangement $(m_1 \ldots m_N)$; i.e. n_j is the number of times j occurs in the set of numbers $m_1 \ldots m_N$. It is convenient to assume that ω_1 and ω_0 are both equal to 1. The latter assumption is permissible because the number of empty cells is determined by the numbers of doubly, trebly ... occupied cells, since the number of cells is equal to the number of molecules.

Equation (1) would be exactly correct if most of the cells contained one molecule and all the multiply occupied cells and empty cells were remote from each other. However, it neglects interactions between different multiply occupied or empty cells, corresponding for example to the fact that the introduction of one doubly occupied and one empty cell would affect the configuration integral differently according as the two cells concerned were adjacent or remote. In fact (1) seems to be a useful approximation at densities not much higher than the critical density, but is probably less satisfactory at higher densities.

The idea behind (1) is that the effect of a given multiply occupied cell on the restricted configuration integral depends only on the *local* conditions. With this in mind it would not be difficult to generalize the equation to make it as accurate as necessary. Thus one might assume instead of (1) the form

$$Q^{(m_1 \ldots m_N)} = Q^{(1 \ldots 1)} \prod_j \omega_j{}^{n_j} \prod \zeta_{ik}^{n_{ik}} \qquad (6.4.2)$$

in which n_{ik} is the number of nearest neighbour pairs of cells occupied respectively by i and k molecules, and the factors ζ_{ik} allow for interactions between the multiply occupied cells. This equation has not been used in practice, though approximate values of a factor corresponding to $\zeta_{2,0}$ have been calculated.[3]

If the form (1) is assumed two problems remain; to evaluate the quantities ω_j, and then to evaluate the total configuration integral. The second is comparatively straightforward.[9] Substituting (1) in (6.1.2) we find

$$\beta^N = \sum_{\substack{n_0 \ldots n_N \\ \Sigma j n_j = N \\ \Sigma n_j = N}} \prod (\omega_j/j\,!\,)^{n_j} \frac{N\,!}{n_0\,!\,n_1\,!\ldots m_N\,!} \qquad (6.4.3)$$

The sum in (3) may be evaluated by the usual method of selecting the maximum term. The result is

$$\beta = (1/x) \sum_{i=0} (\omega_i/i\,!\,)x^i \qquad (6.4.4)$$

The parameter x appearing in (4) is determined by the equation

$$\sum_{i=0} (\omega_i/i\,!\,)x^i = \sum_{i=1} i(\omega_i/i\,!\,)x^i \qquad (6.4.5)$$

If the values of ω_i are known (5) can be solved for x and β can then be determined from (4).

The central difficulty is of course the evaluation of ω_i. Pople[8] proposed that ω_2 should be approximated by ω_2^*, where

$$\omega_2^* = \frac{\iint \exp\{-[\psi(\mathbf{r}_1) + \psi(\mathbf{r}_2) - 2\psi(0) + u(R_{12})]/kT\}\, d\mathbf{r}_1\, d\mathbf{r}_2}{\left[\int \exp\{-[\psi(\mathbf{r}) - \psi(0)]/kT\}\, d\mathbf{r}\right]^2} \quad (6.4.6)$$

Obviously similar approximations ω_3^*, ω_4^*, etc., could be considered. Equation (6) neglects two important features: (i) that twelve molecules are in cells adjacent to an empty cell and twelve in cells adjacent to a doubly occupied cell; (ii) that the "correlation" effects involving the two molecules in the doubly occupied cells are changed. Extensive calculations on these points were made by Barker[3] for a 12–6 fluid in the neighbourhood of the critical density.

These calculations were based on an approximate cell field derived by averaging $\exp\{-[\psi(\mathbf{r}) - \psi(0)]/kT\}$ over the surface of a sphere rather than $[\psi(\mathbf{r}) - \psi(0)]$; values of ω_2^* depend on the outer part of the cell where the smearing approximation is seriously wrong. It was proposed that ω_2 should be approximated by

$$\omega_2 = \omega_2^* \left(\frac{v_f' \, v_f''}{v_f^2}\right)^{12} \left[\frac{1 + 2f' + f''}{(1+f)^2}\right]^{12} \quad (6.4.7)$$

In (7) the second and third factors make approximate allowance for the features (i) and (ii) mentioned above. The free volumes for cells with one nearest-neighbour cell empty or doubly occupied respectively are denoted by v_f', v_f''. The quantity f' is a correlation factor analogous to f (cf. (6.3.2)) but corresponding to correlations between one of the molecules in a doubly occupied cell and a molecule in a neighbouring cell. Similarly f'' is a *ternary* correlation factor for two molecules in a doubly occupied cell and one in a neighbouring cell. Since the integral defining f'' could not be evaluated f'' was approximated by $(f')^2$; it was expected that f'' would be negative at high densities so that this would seriously overestimate ω_2 at higher densities. For details of the approximate methods used in these calculations we refer to the original publications. Results for $kT/\epsilon = 1\cdot2$ are shown in Table 6.6.

The values of ω_2 rise abruptly as V/V_0 is reduced to $2\cdot0$; this is probably due to the approximation of replacing f'' by $(f')^2$, and indicates that the method of calculation is quite unsatisfactory at high densities. In calculating β it was assumed that ω_3/ω_2, ω_4/ω_3, etc., were equal to

TABLE 6.6

Correlation and multiple occupation effects; 12–6 fluid, $kT/\epsilon = 1\cdot2$

V/V_0	$1 + f$	ω_2^*	ω_3	$(v_f'v_f''/v_f^2)^{12}$	$(1 + f')^{24}/(1 + f)^{24}$	ω_2	β
2·0	1·05	0·013	0·0002	3·77	$0\cdot98 \times 10^4$	—	—
2·4	1·02	0·205	0·037	2·75	1·18	0·66	2·20
2·8	0·98	0·51	0·23	2·16	0·40	0·44	2·07
3·2	0·95	0·73	0·49	1·81	0·39	0·51	2·21
3·6	0·93	0·86	0·72	1·50	0·47	0·62	2·37
4·0	0·93	0·94	0·88	1·38	0·43	0·55	2·33

ω_3^*/ω_2^*. In fact ω_3 had a very small effect and ω_4, etc., negligible effect on the value of β.

These results show the difficulties that arise in estimating the communal free energy even at reasonably low densities. Simple approximations such as (6) do not lead to accurate results. At higher densities (6) would be even more seriously wrong, in the direction of underestimating the effect of multiple occupation.

In Fig. 6.1 we show the corrections to the free energy given by the L-J-D theory required by (i) correction of the error due to the "smearing" approximation, (ii) allowance for correlation effects, (iii) allowance

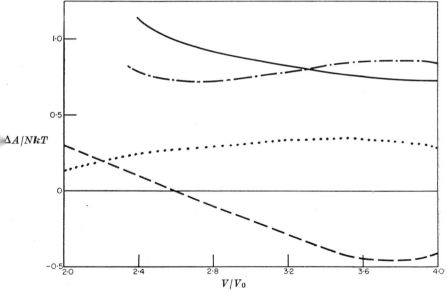

FIG. 6.1. Corrections to L-J-D free energy. Smearing correction shown thus — — —, correlation correction thus · · · · · ·, "communal" correction thus — · — · — · and total correction thus ————. For $kT/\epsilon = 1\cdot2$. (Reproduced with permission from *Proc. Roy. Soc.*)

G

for multiple occupation of cells. The data on which the figure is based
are given in Tables 6.2 and 6.6. In Fig. 6.2 the total correction derived
by summing these three contributions (interpolated to $kT/\epsilon = 1{\cdot}26$) is
compared with the experimentally required correction derived by
calculating the free energy from the critical isotherm for inert gases and

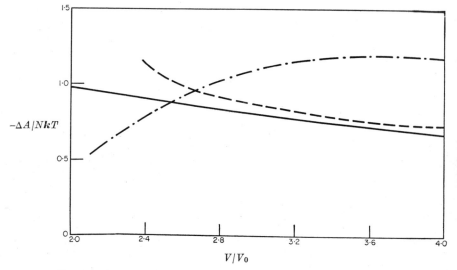

Fig. 6.2. Corrections to L-J-D free energy at critical temperature. Experimentally required correction shown thus ————, Barker's estimate
thus — — —, estimate from de Boer's cell cluster theory thus
—·—·—·. (Reproduced with permission from *Proc. Roy. Soc.*).

subtracting the L-J-D value.[3] Apart from the rather abrupt rise at
high densities ($V/V_0 \simeq 2{\cdot}4$) the theoretically estimated correction is
fairly close to the experimentally required correction. We can at least
understand why the L-J-D theory is in error at low densities. However,
pressures calculated from the "corrected" L-J-D theory are unsatisfactory, because of the spurious rise in free energy at high densities.

6.5   *Prospect for the Cell Theory*

While the theory developed in this chapter contributes to our understanding of the cell model and can in principle be made into an accurate
theory of fluids, it cannot at present be regarded as a satisfactory basis
for a practically useful theory. This is due to the intractable nature of
the problem of evaluating the communal free energy. Even when
V/V_0 is as large as $2{\cdot}4$ the binary occupation factor ω_2 is seriously
affected by *ternary* correlation effects. At the density of the liquid at

the triple point one would probably have to consider the correlated motions of more than three molecules to form a realistic estimate of the communal free energy. This is unlikely to become practicable within the framework of the present cell theory. Essentially similar difficulties occur in the cell cluster theory to be discussed in the next chapter.

There is one possibility for advance within the framework of the existing theory. The importance of correlation effects in the determination of multiple occupation factors arises from the possibility of molecules in neighbouring cells moving over to make more room for the molecules in the multiply occupied cell. When each cell contains one molecule the assumption of independent motions *with neighbouring molecules at their cell centres* gives a reasonably accurate result. But in this case the cell centres are also *equilibrium points*. When a cell is doubly occupied this is no longer the case, and a large part of the "correlation" effect probably arises from this fact. If before starting to evaluate the free volume we determined the lowest energy configuration consistent with two molecules being in one cell, and if we then determined the free volume on the assumption of independent motions (consistent with two molecules remaining in the designated cell) about the equilibrium points of this configuration. we should probably obtain much more satisfactory results. In the theory of solids it is recognized that the energy required to move an atom to an interstitial site is considerably reduced by structural relaxation of surrounding atoms. By recognizing this fact we should in a sense be considering the correlated motions of many molecules, but only to determine the basic configuration about which the molecules are regarded as moving independently. Calculations of this kind seem quite practicable with electronic computing methods, but have not so far been performed.

REFERENCES

1. KIRKWOOD, J. G., *J. chem. Phys.* 1950, **18**, 380.
2. BARKER, J. A., *Proc. roy. Soc.* 1955, **A230**, 390.
3. BARKER, J. A., *Proc. roy. Soc.* 1956, **A237**, 63.
4. TAYLOR, W. J., *J. chem. Phys.* 1956, 24, 454.
5. BUEHLER, R. J., WENTORF, R. H., HIRSCHFELDER, J. O. and CURTISS, C. F., *J. chem. Phys.* 1951, **19**, 61.
6. BARKER, J. A., *Proc. roy. Soc.* 1957, **A240**, 265.
7. BORN, M. and HUANG, K., *Dynamical Theory of Crystal Lattices*, Clarendon Press, Oxford, 1954.
8. SALTER, L., *Proc. roy. Soc.* 1955, **A233**, 418.
9. POPLE, J. A., *Phil. Mag.* 1951, **42**, 459.
10. JANSSENS, P., and Prigogine, I. *Physica* 1950, **16**, 895.

CHAPTER 7

THE CELL CLUSTER THEORY

7.1 Cell Clusters[1, 3-6]

We have discussed in chapter 6 the correlation and multiple occupation effects which are ignored by the L-J-D theory. The cell cluster theory, developed by de Boer,[1] provides an elegant and formally convergent method for taking account of these effects. Unlike the theory of chapter 6, which treats the correlation and multiple occupation effects separately, the cell cluster theory treats them simultaneously. This leads to a considerable gain in formal simplicity.

The basic idea is to divide the lattice of cells into *clusters* of cells and to express the total configuration integral as a sum of products of cell cluster configuration integrals. The simplest of these integrals is the L-J-D free volume v_f, and the leading term in the sum of products is just the L-J-D result for the configuration integral. The remaining terms involve contributions from pairs or larger clusters of cells, and correct for correlation and multiple occupation effects. In practice the only clusters for which the integrals can be evaluated are *pairs* of cells. If only the contributions from these are included then the cell cluster theory suffers from roughly the same limitations as the theory described in chapter 6.

We consider a *cluster* of l cells $\alpha, \beta \dots \lambda$; we suppose that the cluster is *connected* in the sense that any two cells in the cluster are connected by a nearest-neighbour chain of cells also in the cluster. For this particular cluster of cells we define a cell cluster integral by the relation

$$Q'_{\alpha, \beta \dots \lambda} = \frac{1}{l!} \int \dots \int_{\text{cluster}} \exp\left\{ -\left[\psi(\mathbf{r}_1 \dots \mathbf{r}_l) - \psi(0 \dots 0|\right]/kT\right\} \, d\mathbf{r}_1 \dots d\mathbf{r}$$

$$(7.1.1)$$

In this expression $[\psi(\mathbf{r}_1 \dots \mathbf{r}_l) - \psi(0 \dots 0)]$ denotes the change of potential energy when the l molecules in the cluster of l cells are moved from a configuration in which there is one molecule at the centre of each cell to their actual positions at $\mathbf{r}_1 \dots \mathbf{r}_l$. The molecules in all cells not in the cluster are assumed to be at their cell centres. This change of potential energy will involve both a change in the mutual potential energy of the l molecules in the cluster and a change in the interaction of these l molecules with others outside the cluster. In the integral in (1) all the l molecules are assumed to range through the whole volume of the cluster.

Clearly $Q'_{\alpha,\beta\ldots\lambda}$ is a generalization of the single-cell free volume. In particular Q'_α is just equal to the ordinary free volume v_{f}. The value of $Q'_{\alpha,\beta\ldots\lambda}$ depends only on the *number* and *relative arrangement* of the cells $\alpha,\ \beta\ldots\lambda$. Thus we could also write $Q'_{\alpha,\beta\ldots\lambda}$ as $Q'_{l,k}$ where l specifies the *number* of cells in the cluster and k the arrangement. In particular when l is 1 or 2 there is only one possible arrangement of the cells, so that the second subscript may be omitted.

We now define a set of quantities $v_{l,k}$ in terms of the $Q'_{l,k}$ by the relations

$$Q'_1 = v_1 \tag{7.1.2}$$

$$Q'_2 = v_2 + v_1^2 \tag{7.1.3}$$

$$Q'_{l,k} = \sum_{d(l,k)} \prod_{l'k'} v_{l'k'} \tag{7.1.4}$$

The summation in (4) is taken over all possible divisions $d(l, k)$ of the connected cluster (l, k) into equal or smaller connected clusters (l', k'). Clearly (2) and (3) are particular cases of (4). Since each equation of the type (4) introduces one new $v_{l,k}$ it is easy to solve successively for the $v_{l,k}$. In particular we find

$$v_1 = Q'_1 \tag{7.1.5}$$

$$v_2 = Q'_2 - (Q'_1)^2 \tag{7.1.6}$$

Using (4) the total configuration integral for a system of N molecules can be expressed in the form

$$\begin{aligned} Q &= Q'_N \exp\left(-U_0/kT\right) \\ &= v_1^N \exp\left(-U_0/kT\right) \sum_{d(N)} \prod_{l'k'} w_{l',k'} \end{aligned} \tag{7.1.7}$$

In (7) we have used the symbol $w_{l',k'}$ for $v_{l',k'}/v_1^{l'}$. This equation is of course an identity if all terms are included. Its practical usefulness rests on the fact that $w_{l,k}$ for clusters containing many cells can be expected to be small.

In a given division of the N cells into clusters we shall denote the number of (l, k) clusters by $m_{l,k}$. The notation $\{m_{l,k}\}$ will be used for the whole set of numbers m_1, m_2, etc. The number of different divisions of the N cells into clusters corresponding to a given set $\{m_{l,k}\}$ will be denoted by $g(\{m_{l,k}\})$. It is to be noted that $g(\{m_{l,k}\})$ is a function of all the numbers m_1, m_2, etc. With these definitions we can rewrite (7) in the form

$$Q = Q_{\text{L-J-D}} \sum_{\{m_{l,k}\}}' g(\{m_{l,k}\}) \prod_{l,k} w_{l,k}{}^{m_{l,k}} \qquad (7.1.8)$$

$$Q_{\text{L-J-D}} = v_1^N \exp\left(-U_0/kT\right) \qquad (7.1.9)$$

The configuration integral given by the L-J-D theory is denoted by $Q_{\text{L-J-D}}$. The summation in (8) is to be taken over all sets $\{m_{l,k}\}$ which are geometrically possible in that they correspond to real divisions of the N cells into cell clusters.

The result expressed by (8) is the formal basis of the cell cluster theory. To find explicit results it is necessary first to evaluate the quantities $w_{l,k}$, and then to evaluate $g(\{m_{l,k}\})$ and perform the summation. The latter problem is a combinatorial problem of a kind which has been considered extensively in connection with the lattice model for polymer solutions. It can be solved exactly only for a one-dimensional system, but satisfactory approximate methods are known for two- and three-dimensional systems.

We shall assume that the quantities $w_{l,k}$ for clusters of three or more cells can be neglected. In these circumstances (8) becomes

$$Q = Q_{\text{L-J-D}} \sum_{m_1, m_2}' g(m_1, m_2) w_2{}^{m_2} \qquad (7.1.10)$$

where $g(m_1, m_2)$ is the number of ways of dividing the N cells into m_1 single cells and m_2 clusters of two (connected) cells. In the language of the theory of polymer solutions $g(m_1, m_2)$ is the number of ways of distributing m_2 dimers on a lattice of $N = m_1 + 2m_2$ sites. According to the well-known Miller–Guggenheim formula[2] $g(m_1, m_2)$ is given approximately by

$$g(m_1, m_2) = \left(\frac{z}{2}\right)^{m_2} \frac{(m_1 + 2m_2)!}{m_1!\, m_2!} \left[\frac{(m_1 + 2(z-1)m_2/z)!}{(m_1 + 2m_2)!}\right]^{z/2} \qquad (7.1.11)$$

with the restricting condition

$$m_1 + 2m_2 = N \qquad (7.1.12)$$

In (11) z is the coordination number of the lattice.

Using (11) and (12) the summation in (10) may be evaluated; the result is

$$Q = Q_{\text{L-J-D}} \left[\frac{(1-x)^{z/2}}{1-zx}\right]^N \qquad (7.1.13)$$

$$x = \frac{\{2zw_2 + 1 - \sqrt{[4(z-1)w_2 + 1]}\}}{2(z^2w_2 + 1)} \qquad (7.1.14)$$

Originally Cohen et al.[3] derived these equations by a different treatment of the combinatorial problem, not involving the use of the Miller–Guggenheim formula. Although (13) and (14) are approximate the error introduced by them is probably less than the error involved in neglecting $w_{3,k}$, etc.

7.2 Some Detailed Results

The remaining problem of the cell cluster theory is the determination of the quantity w_2, defined by

$$w_2 = [Q_2' - (Q_1')^2]/(Q_1')^2 \qquad (7.2.1)$$

In evaluating Q_2' contributions arise from configurations with both molecules in the same cell with the other cell empty, and also from configurations with one molecule in each cell of the cluster. In fact in the notation of chapter 6, w_2 is given by

$$w_2 = f + \zeta_{2,0}\omega_2^* \qquad (7.2.2)$$

The first term f arises from the configurations with one molecule in each cell (cf. (6.3.2)) while the second term arises from configurations with the two molecules in one cell (cf. (6.4.2), (6.4.6)). The factor $\zeta_{2,0}$ is included because the doubly occupied cell is always adjacent to an empty cell. At high densities the second term in (2) is negligible compared with the first and f is also small. In these circumstances the cell cluster theory leads to results essentially identical with those found in chapter 6 by neglecting the "communal" free energy. At lower densities the second term in (2) becomes important.

Cohen and Rethmeier[6] evaluated w_2 exactly for a two-dimensional system of rigid spheres and compared the calculated pressures with values derived from Monte Carlo calculations. The agreement of the cell cluster theory with the Monte Carlo values was unsatisfactory. In particular the correction to the L-J-D results introduced by considering clusters of two cells appeared to be of the wrong sign over a considerable range of density. Presumably if terms corresponding to sufficiently large clusters were included this correction would be reversed. However the cell cluster theory, with allowance for two-cell clusters only, does not improve on the L-J-D theory as far as the pressure is concerned, although the entropy is certainly improved. The difficulty with the pressure is essentially the same as the difficulty of the communal free energy discussed in chapter 6. The substantial positive correction to the pressure introduced by considering two-cell clusters occurs in the density range where the configurations with two molecules in one cell become significant. Because we consider molecules in neighbouring cells as fixed at their cell centres we underestimate considerably the density at which this occurs (cf. section 6.5). Thus if we could include contributions from much larger clusters we would probably find that the substantial positive correction to the pressure would occur around $A/A_0 = 1.5$ instead of around $A/A_0 = 2.5$.

Earlier approximate calculations for the three-dimensional rigid sphere system[5] indicated that the corrections required by the two-cell cluster theory are qualitatively of the right nature except that they are shifted in the direction of increased volumes. This is consistent with the behaviour of the two-dimensional system and with the explanation suggested above.

Apart from some results for harmonic force models the only values of w_2 available for realistic potential functions are some approximate values for the 12–6 potential calculated by Barker.[8] The results for $kT/\epsilon = 1.2$ are shown in Table 7.1. As well as w_2 we show the separate contributions from configurations with the two molecules in different cells (f) and in the same cell ($\zeta_{2,0}\omega_2^*$). For V/V_0 greater than about 2·4 the contribution f is swamped by $\zeta_{2,0}\omega_2^*$; the result of this is that the calculated correction to the pressure is positive, whereas it should be negative. This is of course another example of the behaviour found with the rigid sphere systems. We have plotted the calculated correction to the L-J-D free energy of the 12–6 fluid at the critical temperature in Fig. 6.2. Although the correction is of the right sign and magnitude its variation with volume is not in agreement with the experimentally required correction. In this respect the theory of chapter 6 appears to be more satisfactory.

TABLE 7.1

Approximate values of w_2 (and f and $\zeta_{2,0}\omega_2^*$) for the 12–6 potential,
$$kT/\epsilon = 1.2$$

V/V_0	2·0	2·4	2·8	3·2	3·6	4·0
f	0·05	0·02	−0·02	−0·05	−0·07	−0·07
$\zeta_{2,0}\omega_2^*$	0·04	0·22	0·46	0·62	0·72	0·77
w_2	0·09	0·23	0·44	0·57	0·65	0·70

7.3 *Discussion*

The cell cluster theory is formally satisfying, and there is no doubt that if one could evaluate the quantities $w_{l,k}$ for *large* clusters it would give satisfactory results for liquids and solids. In practice only w_2 can be evaluated, and in these circumstances the theory does not seem to give very satisfactory results except for solids. In fact the formally much less pleasing theory of chapter 6 is apparently better at low densities. To some extent it seems that what the cell cluster theory gains in simplicity and elegance it loses in flexibility. Of course if it becomes practicable to evaluate the quantities $w_{l,k}$ for larger clusters this situation will be changed entirely.

An advantage of the cell cluster theory is that it can easily be carried over into quantum mechanics, simply by replacing the classical cluster integrals by quantal Slater sums. Cohen et al.[4] used this approach to calculate specific heats for crystals at low temperatures, and showed that the results agreed with those derived from the more usual Born–Kármán approach.

Recently Dahler and Cohen[7] have generalized the cell cluster theory in such a way as to allow for the presence of holes or empty cells. The consequences of this modification are not yet known, but it seems likely that the equilibrium number of holes would be so small in the neighbourhood of the triple point that they would have very little effect on the liquid properties in that temperature range (cf. chapter 5).

REFERENCES

1. DE BOER, J., *Physica* 1954, **20**, 655.
2. GUGGENHEIM, E. A., *Mixtures*, Clarendon Press, Oxford; ch. X, 1952.
3. COHEN, E. G. D., DE BOER, J. and SALSBURG, Z. W., *Physica* 1955, **21**, 137.
4. COHEN, E. G. D., DE BOER, J. and SALSBURG, Z. W., *Physica* 1957, **23**, 389.
5. SALSBURG, Z. W., COHEN, E. G. D., RETHMEIER, B. C. and DE BOER, J., *Physica* 1957, **23**, 400.
6. COHEN, E. G. D. and RETHMEIER, B. C., *Physica* 1958, **24**, 959.
7. DAHLER, J. S. and COHEN, E. G. D., *Physica* 1960, **26**, 81.
8. BARKER, J. A., *Proc. roy. Soc.* 1956, **A237**, 63.

CHAPTER 8

HOLE THEORIES OF LIQUIDS

8.1 *"Cell" and "Hole" Theories*

The ideas motivating "hole" theories have already been discussed briefly in section 3.3. We are now in a position to understand the relation between cell and hole theories more clearly. In chapter 6 we saw that the configuration integral for a system of molecules can be expressed formally as a sum of terms corresponding to different modes of occupation of the cells of an arbitrary lattice of cells. Neglecting all terms in this sum except that corresponding to single occupation of all the cells leads to the L-J-D theory. The remaining terms take account of "communal" effects, and we have seen that these terms are difficult to evaluate satisfactorily.

This analysis was based on the assumption that the number of cells was equal to the number of molecules. But this assumption is by no means necessary. We can make a similar formal analysis for *any* division of the available volume into cells. If the number of cells exceeds the number of molecules then there will be a number of empty cells or holes present even when no cell contains more than one molecule. Furthermore one may hope that by choosing the cells sufficiently small it can be arranged that configurations in which any cell contains more than one molecule contribute negligibly to the configuration integral. If this were possible then the additional disorder of the liquid state as compared with the solid state would be described in terms of the ways of distributing N molecules with 1 or 0 in each of L cells, with L greater than N; the difficult "communal" problem would be circumvented entirely.

Hole theories are based largely on this idea, that the cells can be chosen sufficiently small so that configurations with more than one molecule in any cell can be neglected entirely. This is not obviously true. It can be argued that if the cells are big enough to contain *one* molecule they are also big enough to contain *two*, since a co-operative displacement of a large number of molecules can bring about a situation in which many molecules lie close to the boundaries of their cells, and further small displacements can bring two molecules into many cells. We saw in section 6.3 that even if the cells are as small as the molecular volume of the liquid at the triple point the "communal" free energy remains apparently significant. Thus there is some doubt as to the justification for the assumption that multiple occupation of cells can be neglected in the hole theories. Nevertheless this assumption has been made in existing hole theories.

Whether for this reason or because of other simplifying approximations which are introduced, the results that have been obtained with hole theores are not encouraging. At high densities the number of holes is so small that their effects on the thermodynamic properties are almost negligible (cf. Table 5.2). Thus in the high density region the hole theories, like the L-J-D theory, must be regarded as describing solids rather than liquids. As far as lower densities are concerned the calculated values of critical constants that have been derived depend strongly on the detailed approximations that are made, and are not in good agreement with experimental data.

Our detailed discussion of hole theories will be based in part on an analysis of these theories due to Rowlinson and Curtiss.[1] We have mentioned in chapter 5 the hole theory of Levine et al.[2] which was based on the variational method. We shall not discuss this work in detail because of the conclusion reached in chapter 5 that the variational method is not superior to the simpler L-J-D approach. We have also mentioned in chapter 7 the work of Dahler and Cohen[3] on the cell cluster theory with holes. This is no doubt the most satisfactory approach to a hole theory, but the results obtained with simpler hole theories suggest that the improvement to be expected in the cell cluster theory as a result of allowing for the presence of holes is not large.

8.2 Formal Analysis

As in section 6.1 we consider an arbitrary division of the available volume V into a lattice of cells. However, we now suppose that the number of L of cells is not necessarily equal to the number N of molecules. Corresponding to (6.1.1) we can express the configuration integral in the form

$$Q = \frac{1}{N!} \sum_{\substack{m_1 \ldots m_L \\ \Sigma m_s = N}} Q^{(m_1 \ldots m_L)} \left(\frac{N!}{\prod_s m_s!} \right) \qquad (8.2.1)$$

Like (6.1.1) this is simply a formal classification of configurations. However we now assume that it is permissible to neglect all the

$Q^{(m_1 \ldots m_L)}$ except those for which the numbers $m_1 \ldots m_L$ are all 0 or 1. Thus (1) becomes

$$Q = \sum_{\substack{m_s = 0,1 \\ \Sigma m_s = N}} Q^{(m_1 \ldots m_L)} \tag{8.2.2}$$

We seek to evaluate (2) using the assumptions of the L-J-D theory. If we use the approximation of independent motions (thus neglecting correlation effects) we find a result exactly analogous to (3.3.2):

$$Q = \sum_{\lambda} \prod (v_f^{i\lambda}) \exp\left(-U_{0\lambda}/\boldsymbol{k}T\right) \tag{8.2.3}$$

The summation $\sum_{\lambda}$ in (3) is taken over all arrangements λ of the molecules with not more than one in any cell. Arrangements differing only by a permutation of the molecules are regarded as identical (in (3.3.2) these are regarded as *different* arrangements, so that a factor $1/N$! appears). The potential energy of arrangement λ when the molecules are at their cell centres is denoted by $U_{0\lambda}$, and $v_f^{i\lambda}$ is the free volume for the molecule i in arrangement λ.

We will now suppose that interactions between molecules in cells that are not nearest neighbours can be neglected. If ω_i'' denotes the fraction of the cells adjacent to cell i which are vacant (in a particular arrangement λ) and if $E(0)$ is the energy of interaction of two molecules at the centres of neighbouring cells, then we have

$$U_{0\lambda} = \tfrac{1}{2} zE(0)(N - X_{\lambda}) \tag{8.2.4}$$

$$X_{\lambda} = \sum_{i} \omega_i \tag{8.2.5}$$

where z is the number of nearest-neighbour cells.

The free volume $v_f^{i\lambda}$ depends on the number of the cells adjacent to i which are occupied. It also depends on the *arrangement* of the occupied cells about the cell i. If, however, we use the smearing approximation to evaluate $v_f^{i\lambda}$ this dependence on the arrangement of the neighbouring occupied cells disappears, and we find

$$v_f^{i\lambda} = j(\omega_i) \tag{8.2.6}$$

$$j(\omega) = \int_{\text{cell}} \exp\left\{-(1 - \omega)[\psi(\rho) - \psi(0)]/\boldsymbol{k}T\right\} d\mathbf{r} \tag{8.2.7}$$

In (7) $[\psi(\rho) - \psi(0)]$ is the "smeared" cell field which would be found if all cells were occupied (cf. (4.3.1)). It seems likely that the "smearing" approximation is rather more drastic when an appreciable number of cells are empty than when all cells are occupied.

According to (7) $j(\omega)$ is the L-J-D free volume corresponding to the given cell volume and to the temperature $T/(1 - \omega)$. Thus $j(\omega)$ can be evaluated from existing tabulations (see chapter 4 for references). Unfortunately, however, the summation in (3) cannot be evaluated easily unless $j(\omega)$ depends on ω in a particularly simple way. It is usually assumed that $\ln j(\omega)$ can be approximated by a linear function of ω:

$$\ln j(\omega) = \omega \ln j_1 + (1 - \omega) \ln j_0 \qquad (8.2.8)$$

In (8) j_1 and j_0 are constants; since (8) is only an approximation j_1 and j_0 are not necessarily equal to $j(1)$ and $j(0)$, respectively.

Rowlinson and Curtiss show that the representation of $\ln j(\omega)$ as a linear function of ω is a poor approximation if ω is to range between 0 and 1. Nevertheless it is reasonable to suppose that values of ω in the neighbourhood of the *average* value for a given temperature and density are most important in (3), so that reasonable results might be expected if the constants j_0 and j_1 are chosen so that (8) is accurate in this region. We shall consider several ways of choosing j_0 and j_1 in section 8.3.

If the form (8) is assumed for $j(\omega)$, (3) becomes

$$Q = j_0^N \exp\left(-\tfrac{1}{2}zNE(0)/kT\right) \sum_\lambda \exp\left(X_\lambda \zeta/kT\right) \qquad (8.2.9)$$

$$\zeta = \tfrac{1}{2}zE(0) + kT \ln (j_1/j_0) \qquad (8.2.10)$$

The point of using the form (8) is that the product $\prod v_f^{j\lambda}$ in (3) depends only on X_λ. If $g(N, L, X)$ is the number of arrangements of the N molecules on L lattice sites with X nearest-neighbour pairs of one occupied and one unoccupied cells, (9) may be written

$$Q = j_0^N \exp\left(-\tfrac{1}{2}zNE(0)/kT\right) \sum_X g(N, L, X) \exp\left(X\zeta/kT\right) \qquad (8.2.11)$$

The summation in (11) may be evaluated approximately by the method of Bethe[4] or the equivalent "quasichemical" method of Guggenheim.[5] The result is

$$Q = \frac{L!}{(L - N)! \, N!} j_0^N \exp\left(-\tfrac{1}{2}zNE(0)/kT\right) \times$$

$$\times \left[\frac{x(\beta + 1 - 2x)}{(1 - x)(\beta - 1 + 2x)}\right]^{\frac{1}{2}zN} \left[\frac{(1 - x)(\beta + 1)}{\beta + 1 - 2x}\right]^{\frac{1}{2}zL} \qquad (8.2.12)$$

$$x = N/L \qquad (8.2.13)$$

$$\beta^2 = 1 - 4x(1 - x)[1 - \exp\left(-2\zeta/zkT\right)] \qquad (8.2.14)$$

The average value of ω is given by

$$\bar{\omega} = 2(1 - x)/(\beta + 1) \tag{8.2.15}$$

At high densities we expect the number of holes to become very small so that x approaches 1. In these conditions we find the high density limiting form for Q which is equivalent to the L-J-D result:

$$Q = j_0^N \exp\left(-\tfrac{1}{2}zNE(0)/kT\right) \tag{8.2.16}$$

At low densities if the cell volume remains finite the number of holes becomes large and L is much larger than N; in these conditions (12) leads to the low-density limiting form

$$Q = e^N(V/N)^N \tag{8.2.17}$$

This is of course the correct perfect gas result. Thus the configuration integral given by (12) passes continuously from the L-J-D form at high densities to the correct perfect gas result at low densities. This suggests that the "communal" effects have been taken into account. In this connection, however, the remarks of section 8.1 must be remembered.

8.3   *Approximations for $j(\omega)$*

In order to make use of the equations (8.2.12)–(8.2.15) it is necessary to decide on the cell volume, which may be constant or else chosen at each density and temperature to minimize the free energy. It is also necessary to choose the constants j_0 and j_1 which specify the approximate formula (8.2.8) for the free volume. Rowlinson and Curtiss consider four different approximations which we now describe.

(i) The approximation of Cernuschi and Eyring.[6] The cell volume is taken to be constant and equal to its value in the crystal at zero temperature and pressure. Both j_0 and j_1 are set equal to $j(0)$, so that the free volume is approximated by its value when all cells are occupied.

(ii) The approximation of Ono.[7] The cell volume is taken to be constant and equal to its value in the crystal at zero temperature and pressure. The quantities j_0 and j_1 are set equal to $j(0)$ and $j(1)$, respectively, so that the free volume is approximated by linear interpolation between the extreme cases in which all neighbouring cells are filled and empty.

(iii) The approximation of Peek and Hill.[8] The cell volume is determined by minimizing the free energy. Both j_0 and j_1 are set equal to $j(\bar{\omega})$ where $\bar{\omega}$ is the average value of ω determined by (8.2.15). The free volume for all cells is taken as approximately equal to the free volume for a cell with the *average* number of neighbouring holes.

(iv) The approximation of Rowlinson and Curtiss.[1] The cell volume is determined by minimizing the free energy, and j_0 and j_1 determined by

$$\ln j_0 = \ln j\,(\bar\omega) - \bar\omega[\partial \ln j(\omega)/\partial \omega]_{\omega=\bar\omega} \tag{8.3.1}$$

$$\ln j_1 = \ln j(\bar\omega) + (1 - \bar\omega)[\partial \ln j(\omega)/\partial \omega]_{\omega=\bar\omega} \tag{8.3.2}$$

The effect of this is that the $\ln j(\omega)$ versus ω curve is approximated by its tangent at $\omega = \bar\omega$.

Rowlinson and Curtiss examined the consequences of these approximations at low densities by evaluating the second virial coefficient and at intermediate densities by evaluating the critical constants. They found that approximation (i) gave values of the second virial coefficient which were considerably too low at all temperatures, (ii) gave values which were considerably too high at all temperatures, while (iii) and (iv) gave values much closer to the correct values, though still a little too high. This suggested that either of the approximations (iii) or (iv) might give better results at low and intermediate densities than the L-J-D theory, which gives the value zero for the second virial coefficient. This proved not to be the case. In a comparison with the experimental pressure–volume isotherm for hydrogen at 0°C neither the L-J-D theory nor the approximation (iv) gave satisfactory agreement; if anything the L-J-D theory was to be preferred. The values for the critical constants found with the approximations (i)–(iii) are given in Table 8·1, with the L-J-D values and experimental values for argon for comparison. Values for the approximation (iv) are not available.

TABLE 8·1

Critical constants from hole theories, compared with L-J-D and experimental values for argon

	$p_c V_c/RT_c$	kT_c/ϵ	$p_c V_0/N\epsilon$	V_c/V_0	$\bar\omega_c$
Experimental, argon	0·292	1·26	0·116	3·16	—
L-J-D	0·591	1·30	0·434	1·77	0·000
Cernuschi and Eyring	0·342	2·74	0·469	2·00	0·455
Ono	0·342	0·75	0·128	2·00	0·455
Peek and Hill	0·719	1·18	0·261	3·25	0·175

The approximations of Cernuschi and Eyring and of Ono are clearly unsatisfactory, since the predicted critical temperatures are much too high for the former and much too low for the latter. The approximation of Peek and Hill gives critical constants which are in poor agreement with the experimental values for argon, but apparently in somewhat better agreement than the values derived from the L-J-D theory. In particular the critical pressure is only about twice the experimental value, whereas the L-J-D value is almost four times the experimental value.

There is, however, another reason why the theory of Peek and Hill cannot be regarded as satisfactory. The hole theory was developed on the assumption that the cells were to be so small that double or multiple occupation would be very unlikely. But the calculations indicate that only the fraction 0·175 of the cells are empty at the critical point, so that the cell volume is about five-sixths of the critical molecular volume. We have seen in chapter 6 that double occupation of cells is quite probable and has a substantial effect on the thermodynamic properties when the cell is of this size. Thus the approximation of Peek and Hill, and similarly that of Rowlinson and Curtiss, lead to contradictions when applied at densities close to or below the critical density. The theory assumes that the cell is so small that double occupation is negligible, but the cell volume determined by minimizing the free energy does not satisfy this assumption. The approximations of Cernuschi and Eyring and of Ono, in which the cell volume remains fixed, are free of this objection, but they are in any case in poor agreement with experiment.

8.4 Conclusions

Although the hole theories based on the approximations of Peek and Hill or Rowlinson and Curtiss appear to be superior to the L-J-D theory in that they give approximately correct second virial coefficients, this superiority does not extend to higher densities. The critical constants calculated from the approximation of Peek and Hill are unsatisfactory (though better than the L-J-D values). The work of Dahler and Hirschfelder (cf. chapter 5) shows that hole theories cannot be expected to improve on the L-J-D theory at densities as high as the density of the liquid at the triple point. However, in the region of the critical density some improvement seems to follow from the introtion of holes.

The least satisfactory feature is that if the cell volume is determined to minimize the free energy then the cells are so large that multiple occupation cannot be neglected. Thus to develop a really satisfactory hole theory it would probably be necessary to allow for the effects of multiple occupation by the methods of chapter 6 or chapter 7. If this were done it should in principle be possible to calculate the configuration integral correctly with *any* division of the volume into cells. The advantage of choosing a division with more cells than molecules, and therefore with some holes, would be that it would reduce the importance of configurations in which cells are occupied by many molecules. This gain is to be balanced against the disadvantages due to the added complexity of the theory.

REFERENCES

1. ROWLINSON, J. S. and CURTISS, C. F., *J. chem. Phys.* 1951, **19**, 1519.
2. LEVINE, S., MAYER, J. E. and AROESTE, H., *J. chem. Phys.* 1957, **26**, 207.
3. DAHLER, J. S. and COHEN, E. G. D., *Physica* 1960, **26**, 81.
4. BETHE, H. A., *Proc. roy. Soc.* 1935, **A150**, 552.
5. GUGGENHEIM, E. A., *Mixtures*, Clarendon Press, Oxford, ch. IV, 1952.
6. CERNUSCHI, F. and EYRING, H., *J. chem. Phys.* 1939, **7**, 547.
7. ONO, S., *Mem. Faculty of Eng., Kyushu Univ.* 1947, **10**, 190.
8. PEEK, H. M. and HILL, T. L., *J. chem. Phys.* 1950, **18**, 1252.

CHAPTER 9

THE TUNNEL THEORY

9.1 *The Tunnel Model*[1,2]

The tunnel model was introduced in section 3.5, where it was applied to the rigid-sphere fluid. We now wish to develop the tunnel theory in more detail and to apply it to the case of molecules interacting according to the 12–6 potential.

The basic idea of the tunnel theory is that we imagine the whole system of molecules divided into sub-systems consisting of lines of molecules moving almost one-dimensionally in tunnels whose walls are formed by neighbouring lines. In section 3.5 we assumed that the lines were arranged with respect to each other in a two-dimensional close-packed structure, since this leads to the densest possible packing of the kind envisaged by the tunnel model. It is not at first sight obvious that the same arrangement would be chosen by 12–6 molecules, since some other arrangement might be favoured energetically. However, calculations show[2] that the close-packed arrangement leads to considerably lower energy than a two-dimensional square arrangement of the lines of molecules which seems the most likely alternative. We shall therefore base our consideration of the tunnel theory for 12–6 molecules on the close-packed arrangement.

Thus we imagine the volume V divided into hexagonal prisms arranged in two-dimensional close-packing. According to equation (3.5.1) the volume per molecule is related to the average distance l between molecules in a tunnel and the distance r between the axes of neighbouring tunnels by the equation

$$\frac{V}{N} = \frac{\sqrt{3}}{2} r^2 l \qquad (9.1.1)$$

We assume that the molecules in a given tunnel may be considered as moving independently of those in other tunnels. We adopt the smearing approximation, so that in calculating the potential energy of interaction of a given molecule with molecules in other tunnels we consider the neighbours as smeared uniformly over the surfaces of cylinders centred on the axis of the central tunnel. We assume also that the *longitudinal* and *transverse* motions of the molecules in a given tunnel may be treated as *separable*, so that the configuration integral is a product of factors for longitudinal and transverse motions. If there are K tunnels each containing M molecules these assumptions lead to an approximate expression for the configuration integral:

$$Q(N, V) = (1/N\,!)[N\,!/(M\,!)^K] \left[\int_0^{lM} \ldots \int_0^{lM} \exp\left(-U'/kT\right) dz_1 \ldots dz_M\right]^K \times$$
$$\times \exp\left(-\tfrac{1}{2}NV(0)/kT\right)A_f^N \quad (9.1.2)$$

$$U' = \sum_{i>j=1}^{M} u(|z_i - z_j|) \quad (9.1.3)$$

$$A_f = 2\pi \int \exp\left\{-[V(\rho) - V(0)]/kT\right\}\rho\,d\rho \quad (9.1.4)$$

In these equations $V(\rho)$ is the potential energy of interaction of a given molecule at distance ρ from the axis of its tunnel with all molecules except those in its own tunnel. The equation (4) for the "free area" A_f is exactly analogous to (4.2.5) for the "free volume" in the L-J-D theory. Equation (2) is identical in form with (3.5.2) apart from the the factor $\exp\left[-\tfrac{1}{2}NV(0)/kT\right]$, which arises from the interaction between molecules in different tunnels when the molecules lie on their tunnel axes. For rigid spherical molecules this interaction does not arise.

The integral appearing in (2) can be expressed in terms of the configuration integral $Q'(M, lM)$ for a one-dimensional system of M molecules in length lM. This leads to the result

$$Q(N, V) = \exp\left[-\tfrac{1}{2}NV(0)/kT - NA_1/RT\right]A_f^N \quad (9.1.5)$$

In (5) A_1 is the molar configurational free energy of the one-dimensional system, defined by

$$\exp\left(-MA_1/RT\right) = Q'(M, lM)$$
$$= (1/M\,!)\int_0^{lM} \ldots \int_0^{lM} \exp\left(-U'/kT\right) dz_1 \ldots dz_M \quad (9.1.6)$$

9.2 The Potential Energy and Free Area

As a consequence of the smearing approximation the potential energy $V(\rho)$ is given by

$$V(\rho) = \sum_i \left(\frac{n_i}{2\pi\zeta_i rl}\right) \int_{-\infty}^{\infty} dz \int_0^{2\pi} u(\sqrt{\{\rho^2 + \zeta_i^2 r^2 - 2\zeta_i r \cos\phi + z^2\}})\zeta_i r\,d\phi$$
$$(9.2.1)$$

In this equation n_i is the number of lines of molecules in the ith neighbour cylindrical shell while $\zeta_i r$ is the radius of the ith shell (i.e. the distance from the axis of the central tunnel to the axis of a tunnel in the ith shell). The equation is analogous to equation (4.3.2) for the cell field in the L-J-D theory. The factor $(n_i/2\zeta_i\pi_i r l)$ is the number of molecules per unit area in the ith neighbour shell. Values of n_i and ζ_i are given in Table 9.1.

TABLE 9.1

Number and distance of neighbouring lines

Number of shell (i)	1	2	3	4
Number of lines (n_i)	6	6	6	12
Distance (ζ_i)	1	$\sqrt{3}$	2	$\sqrt{7}$

For the case of the 12–6 potential the double integral in (1) can be evaluated in terms of complete elliptic integrals. In this way one finds

$$\frac{V(0)}{kT} = 4{\cdot}652C - 7{\cdot}925B \tag{9.2.2}$$

$$\frac{V(\rho) - V(0)}{kT} = CQ(y) - BP(y) \tag{9.2.3}$$

$$y = \rho/r, \quad B = \frac{4\epsilon r}{lkT}\left(\frac{\sigma}{r}\right)^6, \quad C = \frac{4\epsilon r}{lkT}\left(\frac{\sigma}{r}\right)^{12} \tag{9.2.4}$$

For analytic expressions for the functions $P(y)$ and $Q(y)$, and for tabulated values, we refer to the original publication.[2]

Using these results in (9.1.4) we find

$$A_f = r^2S \tag{9.2.5}$$

$$S = 2\pi \int_0^{0{\cdot}52} \exp[BP(y)-CQ(y)]y \, dy \tag{9.2.6}$$

Values of the integral S, evaluated by numerical integration, are tabulated by Barker.[2] Also tabulated are quantities S_B, S_C defined by

$$S_B = \partial S/\partial B \tag{9.2.7}$$

$$S_C = -\partial S/\partial C \tag{9.2.8}$$

The quantities S, S_B, S_C are analogous to the integrals G, g_L, g_M in the L-J-D theory. The upper limit in (6) is chosen so that the free area becomes equal to the actual cross-sectional area of the tunnel in the low-density or high-temperature limiting case (i.e. when B and C become small).

9.3 The One-Dimensional System

The configuration integral for a one-dimensional system of molecules in which only nearest neighbours interact can be evaluated in a number of ways. The well-known result is that the molar configurational free energy is given by

$$\frac{A_1^*}{RT} = -\frac{1}{N} \ln Q'(N, lN)$$

$$= -\frac{p_1 l}{kT} - \ln \left[\int_0^\infty \exp \{-[u(R) + p_1 R]/kT\} \, dR \right] \quad (9.3.1)$$

Here p_1 is the one-dimensional pressure which is related to the length per molecule l by the equation

$$l = \frac{\displaystyle\int_0^\infty R \exp \{-[u(R) + p_1 R]/kT\} \, dR}{\displaystyle\int^\infty \exp \{-[u(R) + p_1 R]/kT\} dR} \quad (9.3.2)$$

For the case of rigid spherical molecules these equations lead immediately to the result used in section 3.5:

$$Q'(N, lN) = e^N (l-D)^N \quad (9.3.3)$$

For 12–6 molecules it is of course not exactly true that only nearest neighbours interact. Exact evaluation of the configuration integral in these circumstances would be difficult though not impossible. However, at the relevant densities the interactions between molecules which are not nearest neighbours are small, and it is a good approximation simply to add to the free energy given by (1) the additional potential energy that would result from interactions between non-nearest neighbours if all molecules were equally spaced with the spacing l.

Thus for the free energy A_1 appearing in equations (9.1.5) and (9.1.6) we assume the value given by

$$\frac{A_1}{RT} = \frac{A_1^*}{RT} + \sum_{n=2}^{\infty} \frac{u(nl)}{kT}$$

$$= \frac{A_1^*}{RT} + \frac{4\epsilon}{kT} \left[0 \cdot 0003 \left(\frac{\sigma}{l}\right)^{12} - 0 \cdot 0173 \left(\frac{\sigma}{l}\right)^6 \right] \quad (9.3.4)$$

where A_1^* is defined by equations (1) and (2). To use these results it is necessary to evaluate numerically the integrals appearing in (1) and (2). A tabulation of these quantities is given by Barker.[2] Actually tabulated are values of l/σ and of the quantity Z defined by

$$Z = \frac{A_1^*}{RT} + \ln \sigma \qquad (9.3.5)$$

They are given as functions of kT/ϵ and of the quantity W defined by

$$W = kT/p_1\sigma \qquad (9.3.6)$$

To determine Z for a particular values of l/σ it is necessary to determine W by inverse interpolation and then to determine Z by direct interpolation. This procedure is necessitated by the fact that (1) and (2) do not give the free energy explicitly as a function of l, but rather give the free energy and l as functions of p_1. The derivative of Z with respect to l, which is required for evaluating the pressure, is given by

$$\partial Z/\partial(l/\sigma) = 1/W \qquad (9.3.7)$$

9.4 The Thermodynamic Functions

Using these results we find an expression for the configurational free energy:

$$\frac{A^*}{NkT} = -\ln \sigma^3 + \tfrac{1}{2}CQ_0 - \tfrac{1}{2}BP_0 + Z - \ln S - 2\ln(r/\sigma)$$
$$+ (4\epsilon/kT)[0{\cdot}0003(\sigma/l)^{12} - 0{\cdot}0173(\sigma/l)^6] \qquad (9.4.1)$$

We have not so far specified r and l, except that they must satisfy (9.1.1). The correct procedure would be to determine the values of r and l which minimize the free energy given by (1), subject to the restriction imposed by (9.1.1). In fact we shall base our consideration of the theory on the simplifying assumption that r and l are equal. With this assumption (9.1.1) gives

$$l = r = \left(\frac{2}{\sqrt{3}} \frac{V}{V_0}\right)^{1/3} \sigma \qquad (9.4.2)$$

where V_0 as usual is $N\sigma^3$. If this result is substituted in (1) the free energy is given as a function of V/V_0, and other thermodynamic functions can be calculated by differentiation. In particular the pressure is given by

$$\frac{pV_0}{N\epsilon} = \left(\frac{V_0}{V}\right)^5 \left(20{\cdot}938 + 9\frac{S_C}{S}\right) - \left(\frac{V_0}{V}\right)^3 \left(23{\cdot}880 + 6\frac{S_B}{S}\right)$$
$$+ \frac{0{\cdot}3497}{W}\left(\frac{kT}{\epsilon}\right)\left(\frac{V_0}{V}\right)^{2/3} + \frac{2}{3}\left(\frac{V_0}{V}\right)\left(\frac{kT}{\epsilon}\right) \qquad (9.4.3)$$

The zero-pressure equilibrium volume is found by setting p equal to zero and solving (3) for (V/V_0). If vapour imperfection is neglected the vapour pressure can be calculated using equation (4.4.10).

9.5   Comparison with Experiment

We compare first (in Table 9.2) the calculated reduced volume, excess energy and excess entropy for zero pressure and $kT/\epsilon = 0.70$ with the corresponding experimental quantities for liquid and solid argon. Included for comparison are the L-J-D values (taken from Table 4.4).

TABLE 9.2

Theoretical and experimental properties at $kT/\epsilon = 0.70$

	Reduced volume, V/V_0	Reduced excess energy, $E'/N\epsilon$	Reduced excess entropy, S'/Nk
Tunnel theory	1·184	−5·9	−4·8
Liquid argon	1·186	−5·96	−3·64
L-J-D theory	1·037	−7·32	−5·51
Solid argon	1·035	−7·14	−5·33

The tunnel theory values of E' and S' are less accurate because their calculation involved numerical differentiation of Z with respect to temperature.

The volume and energy calculated from the tunnel theory are close to the experimental values for liquid argon, indicating that the tunnel theory is a theory of liquids rather than solids. The value of the entropy calculated from the tunnel theory is, however, considerably too low, although closer to the experimental value for liquid argon than the L-J-D value.

At high densities the experimental variation of volume with temperature and pressure are described well by the tunnel theory. This is shown by Fig. 9.1, comparing theoretical and experimental reduced volumes over a range of temperatures, and by Fig. 9.2, which compares theoretical and experimental values of the reduced speed of sound. For liquids the quantity plotted is $(M/N\epsilon)^{1/2}u$ where M is molecular weight and u the speed of sound. For solids the quantity plotted is

$$\left(\frac{M}{N\epsilon}\right)^{1/2}\left[\frac{(1+\sigma)}{3(1-\sigma)}\right]^{1/2}u_l$$

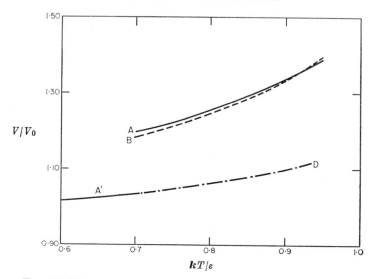

Fig. 9.1. Reduced volumes for 12–6 fluid. Experimental values for liquid argon curve A and for solid argon curve A′. Tunnel theory curve B, L-J-D theory curve D. (Reproduced with permission from *Proc. Roy. Soc.*).

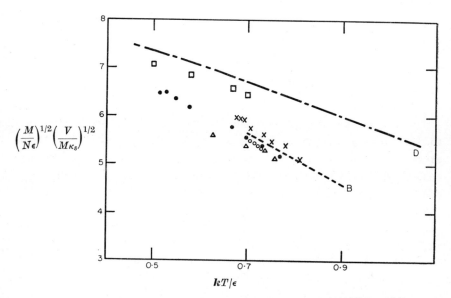

Fig. 9.2. Reduced speed of sound for 12–6 fluid; values of $\left(\dfrac{M}{N\epsilon}\right)^{1/2}\left(\dfrac{V}{M\kappa_s}\right)^{1/2}$ where M is molecular weight and κ_s adiabatic compressibility. Experimental data for liquids listed by Hamann[3] shown thus: argon $\bigcirc$, nitrogen $\times$, oxygen $\bullet$, methane $\triangle$. Experimental data for solid argon[4] shown thus $\square$. Tunnel theory, curve B; cell theory, curve D (personal communication from H. G. David). (Reproduced with permission from *Proc. Roy. Soc.*).

where u_l is the speed of longitudinal waves and σ is Poisson's ratio. In both cases the quantity plotted should be equal to

$$\left(\frac{M}{N\epsilon}\right)^{1/2}\left(\frac{V}{M\kappa_s}\right)^{1/2}$$

where κ_s is the adiabatic compressibility.

The agreement is much less satisfactory at low densities. The calculated critical constants are given in Table 9.3. The tunnel theory values are in slightly worse agreement with experiment than the L-J-D values.

TABLE 9.3

Experimental and theoretical critical constants

	Experimental values, argon	Tunnel theory	L-J-D theory
kT_c/ϵ	1·26	1·07	1·30
V_c/V_0	3·16	1·8	1·77
$p_c V_0/N\epsilon$	0·116	0·37	0·43
$p_c V_c/RT_c$	0·292	0·6	0·59

This is almost certainly due to the approximation of treating the motion in the tunnels as strictly one-dimensional. At high densities it is a good approximation to take the mutual potential energy of the molecules in a given tunnel as U', where

$$U' = \sum_{i>j} u(|z_i - z_j|) \tag{9.5.1}$$

At low densities this approximation becomes less satisfactory, because the molecules can move appreciable distances from the tunnel axis and can adopt a "staggered" arrangement, giving a larger effective free volume. The approximation (1) implies that the second virial coefficient is proportional to

$$\int_0^\infty [1 - \exp\{-u(R)/kT\}]\,dR,$$

instead of the correct

$$\int_0^\infty [1 - \exp\{-u(R)/kT\}]R^2\,dR.$$

This overemphasizes the effect of the repulsive interaction at small distances, leading to pressures which are too high and a critical temperature which is too low. In fact at the experimental critical temperature

$$\int_0^\infty [1 - \exp\{-u(R)/kT\}]\,dR$$

is actually *positive*, while the true second virial coefficient is negative. The L-J-D theory gives zero for the second virial coefficient; thus it is not surprising that the tunnel theory gives slightly worse critical constants than the L-J-D theory. To make the tunnel theory accurate at densities as low as the critical density it would be necessary to avoid the use of the approximation (1), and to take into account the tendency of the molecules to adopt a "staggered" configuration. We shall discuss this further in section 9.6.

Vapour pressures calculated from (9.4.1), (9.4.2) and (4.4.10) are plotted in Fig. 9.3 (curve B). The slope of the curve is close to the slope of the experimental curve for liquid argon (curve A), corresponding to the fact that the calculated energy is close to the experimental value (cf. Table 9.2). However, the calculated values of the logarithm of the

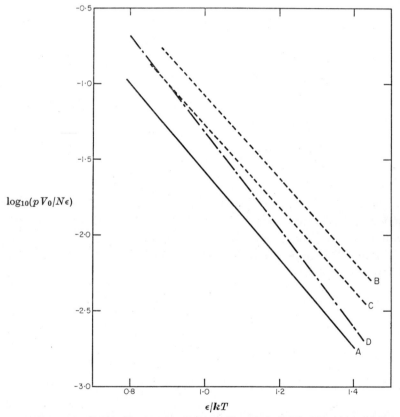

FIG. 9.3. Reduced vapour pressures for 12–6 fluid. Experimental for liquid argon, curve A. Tunnel theory, curve B. Tunnel theory, refined version, curve C. L-J-D theory, curve D. (Reproduced with permission from *Proc. Roy. Soc.*).

vapour pressure are too high by an almost constant amount. This corresponds to the error in the entropy shown in Table 9.2. This is not due to the assumption that l and r are equal; in fact a calculation based on minimizing the free energy with respect to l and r led to a calculated value of $\log_{10}(pV_0/N\epsilon)$ only about 0·05 below the value derived with the assumption $l = r$ (for kT/ϵ close to 0·8).

Approximate calculations have been made to test the effects of the smearing approximation and of the "one-dimensional" approximation expressed by equation (1). For details of these calculations we refer to the original publication.[2] For $kT/\epsilon = 0·7$, $V/V_0 = 1·2$ the results indicated that the calculated free energy should be reduced by about 0·34 NkT to allow for the effect of the smearing approximation and by about 0·11 NkT to allow for the effect of the "one-dimensional" approximation (equation (1)). If it is assumed that these corrections are roughly independent of temperature, then the calculated vapour pressures follow curve C in Fig. 9.3 The agreement with experiment is improved, but a discrepancy remains. The error in the entropy is reduced from about 1·1 Nk to about 0·7 Nk.

9.6   *Discussion*

At high densities the values of pressure and energy (at given volume) or of volume and energy (at given pressure) calculated from the tunnel theory are quite close to the experimental values for liquid argon. This satisfactory agreement suggests strongly that the structures envisaged by the tunnel model are of the same nature as the structures important in liquids, or expressed differently that the tunnel theory is considering the right regions of configuration space. However, the fact that the calculated entropy is too low by about 0·7 Nk suggests that the tunnel theory underestimates the *volume* of configuration space associated with these structures. No doubt the reason for this lies in the assumption that the molecules in different tunnels move independently. We saw in chapter 6 that in the cell theory allowance for correlation effects increased the calculated entropy.

It seems then that further progress with the tunnel theory will require first, a treatment of the motion of the molecules in one tunnel which does not involve the "one-dimensional" approximation of (9.5.1), and second, a treatment of the correlated motions of the molecules in two tunnels which will permit a treatment of correlation effects analogous to that of chapter 6 and chapter 7. Both of these modifications are feasible. The first should improve the agreement between calculated and experimental pressures at low densities, while the second should improve the calculated entropy.

Even in its simplest form the tunnel theory is probably adequate for many purposes. The error in the entropy does not seem to depend greatly on density and temperature, and so is not important if we are concerned with calculating pressures. However, it is important in calculating liquid–gas and liquid–solid equilibria. If we identify the L-J-D condensed phase with the *solid* and the tunnel theory condensed phase with the *liquid*, then the temperature at which the two theoretical vapour pressure curves cross should be the freezing point. But this temperature is much higher than the experimental freezing point ($kT/\epsilon = 0.70$) because the tunnel theory vapour pressure curve is too high.

REFERENCES

1. BARKER, J. A., *Aust. J. Chem.* 1960, **13**, 187.
2. BARKER, J. A., *Proc. roy. Soc.* 1961, **A259**, 442.
3. HAMANN, S. D. *Aust. J. Chem.* 1960, **13**, 325.
4. BARKER, J. R. and DOBBS, E. R., *Phil. Mag.* 1955, **46**, 1069.

CHAPTER 10

THE RADIAL DISTRIBUTION FUNCTION

10.1   *The Experimental Evidence*

So far we have considered the predictions of various lattice theories in regard to the thermodynamic properties of condensed phases. We now turn to the direct structural evidence derived from X-ray and neutron diffraction experiments. Again we shall consider the case of argon, for which both X-ray and neutron diffraction techniques have been used. The X-ray diffraction results of Eisenstein and Gingrich[1] cover a wide range of temperature, from the triple point up to the critical point. The neutron diffraction measurements of Henshaw[2] were made at only one temperature (close to the triple point) but are more accurate than the X-ray results. Comparison between theory and experiment is most conveniently made in terms of the radial distribution function.

10.2   *The Cell Theory*

The problem of calculating the radial distribution function on the basis of the cell model has been considered by a number of authors.[3-5] The calculations we shall consider are based essentially on the L-J-D theory, and involve in particular the assumption that the molecules in different cells move independently. If this assumption is made the calculation is straightforward. The probability $p(r)\,\mathrm{d}r$ that a given molecule is at a distance between r and $r + \mathrm{d}r$ from the centre of its cell is determined by

$$p(r) = r^2 \exp\left[-\{\psi(r) - \psi(0)\}/kT\right] \Big/ \int r^2 \exp\left[-\{\psi(r) - \psi(0)\}/kT\right]\mathrm{d}r$$

$$(10.2.1)$$

The probability $q(R)\,\mathrm{d}R$ that two molecules in different cells with centres separated by the distance a are separated by a distance between R and $R + \mathrm{d}R$ is determined by

$$q(R)\,\mathrm{d}R = \frac{R\,\mathrm{d}R}{4a}\int_0^\infty \mathrm{d}y \int_{|y-a|}^{y+a} \frac{p(r')\,\mathrm{d}r'}{r'} \int_{|y-R|}^{y+R} \frac{p(r)\,\mathrm{d}r}{r} \quad (10.2.2)$$

115

Thus the number density $\rho(R)$ of neighbouring molecules at distance R from a given molecule is determined by

$$4\pi R^2 r(R)\, \mathrm{d}R = \sum_i \frac{m_i R\, \mathrm{d}R}{4a_i} \int_0^\infty \mathrm{d}y \int_{|y-a_i|}^{y+a_i} \frac{p(r')\, \mathrm{d}r'}{r'} \int_{|y-R|}^{y+R} \frac{p(r)\, \mathrm{d}r}{r} \qquad (10.2.3)$$

In (3) the summation with respect to i is taken over the first, second ... neighbour shells; m_i is the number of ith neighbour cells and a_i their distance (cf. section 4.2). Since $p(r)$ is zero when r is greater than $\frac{1}{2}a_1$, the upper limits $y + a_i$ and $y + R$ in (3) may be replaced by $\frac{1}{2}a_1$ (because a_i and hence $y + a_i$ are always greater than $\frac{1}{2}a_1$, and the integration over r' gives zero unless y and hence $y + R$ are greater than $\frac{1}{2}a_1$). Thus we find finally

$$\rho(R) = \frac{1}{16\pi} \sum_i \frac{m_i}{a_i R} \int_0^\infty \mathrm{d}y \int_{|y-a_i|}^{\frac{1}{2}a_1} \frac{p(r')\, \mathrm{d}r'}{r'} \int_{|y-R|}^{\frac{1}{2}a_1} \frac{p(r)\, \mathrm{d}r}{r} \qquad (10.2.4)$$

If the cell field $[\psi(r) - \psi(0)]$ can be approximated by a *harmonic* field Ar^2 the integrations in (4) can be evaluated analytically. Corner and Lennard-Jones[3] made approximate calculations on this basis. Otherwise numerical integration must be used. Rushbrooke[4] calculated $\rho(R)$ for liquid argon at the boiling point using a potential which differed only slightly from the 12–6 potential which we have adopted. His results are compared in Fig. 10.1, with results interpolated to 90°K from the experimental data of Eisenstein and Gingrich.[1]

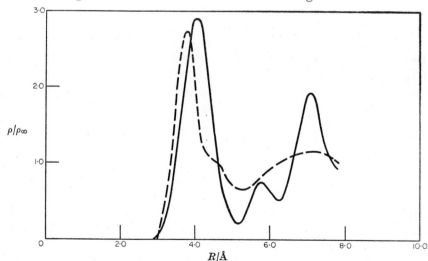

FIG. 10.1. Radial distribution function for argon at 90°K. Experimental data from X-ray diffraction shown thus – – – – – –, Rushbrooke's values calculated from L-J-D theory shown thus ————. (In part reproduced with permission from *Proc. Roy. Soc. Edinb.*).

In Rushbrooke's calculation only interactions with nearest neighbours were considered in calculating the cell field. This would tend to over-estimate the sharpness of the peaks. However, it seems unlikely that inclusion of further neighbour interactions would change the picture seriously. The peaks in the theoretically calculated curve are too sharp. Furthermore the first peak occurs at a distance which is too large. According to the cell theory the first peak is found at a distance which is nearly equal to the distance between neighbouring cell centres. Thus as the temperature is raised and the density falls, the cell theory predicts that the first peak should move to greater distances. But experimentally the distance of the first peak is independent of temperature over a wide range of temperatures.

Corner and Lennard-Jones[3] made a similar calculation for argon at a temperature close to the critical temperature and a density considerably higher than the critical density. Their results are shown in Fig. 10.2.

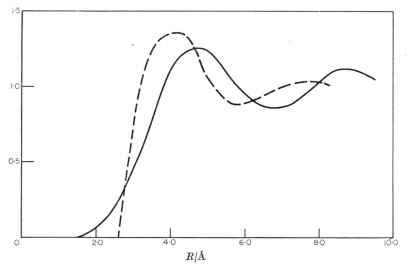

FIG. 10.2. Radial distribution function for argon close to the critical point. Experimental X-ray diffraction data for $kT/\epsilon = 1.25$, $V/V_0 = 2.3$ shown thus $-----$. Results of Corner and Lennard-Jones from L-J-D theory for $kT/\epsilon = 1.33$, $V/V_0 = 2.1$ shown thus $\underline{\hspace{1cm}}$. (Reproduced with permission from *Proc. Roy. Soc.*).

The experimental curve corresponds to a somewhat lower density. However, the differences would be even more marked if the experimental data were available for the same density as the theoretical calculation. The theoretically calculated peaks are much more diffuse than the experimental ones, and the theoretically predicted distance of the first peak is considerably larger than the experimental value. Both these tendencies would be accentuated if the experimental curve corresponded to the same density as the theoretical one.

Thus the cell theory in the L-J-D form predicts peaks that are too sharp at high densities (low temperatures) and peaks that are too diffuse at low densities (high temperatures). Furthermore the predicted distance of the first peak is too large and increases as the density decreases, while the experimental distance remains constant.

No doubt these difficulties would be removed if the correlation and multiple occupation effects discussed in chapters 6 and 7 were correctly taken into account in the calculation. A useful discussion along these lines is given by Green.[6] However, no detailed calculations have yet been performed.

10.3 *Hole Theories*

No detailed calculations of the radial distribution function on the basis of the hole theory have been performed. If the cell size were taken to be independent of density then we should expect that the agreement between the predicted and observed distances of the nearest neighbour peak should be improved at low densities. However, for the more accurate hole theories in which the cell volume is chosen to minimize the free energy (Peek and Hill, Rowlinson and Curtiss; see chapter 8) this would not apply. At high densities the hole theories would give results indistinguishable from those given by the cell theory.

10.4 *The Tunnel Theory*

An approximate calculation of the radial distribution function based on the tunnel theory has been made by Barker[7] for argon at the triple point. In order to make the calculation feasible the "tunnel field" $[V(\rho) - V(0)]$ of chapter 9 was expanded in powers of ρ and terms higher than the quadratic term were neglected. In evaluating the integrals certain approximations were used based on the fact that the coefficient of the quadratic term is large, so that the molecules have low probability of moving far from the tunnel axis. For details of these approximations we refer to the original publication.

The calculated distribution function is compared with the results derived from neutron diffraction by Henshaw in Fig. 10.3. The agreement is excellent, particularly with regard to the first peak. In view of the approximate nature of the calculation this may be partly fortuitous.

However, it suggests that the structural picture on which the tunnel model is based is a useful one.

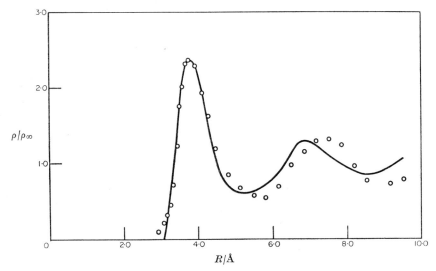

FIG. 10.3. Radial distribution function for liquid argon at 84°K. Neutron diffraction results shown thus ————, Barker's results from tunnel theory shown thus ◯.

REFERENCES

1. EISENSTEIN, A. and GINGRICH, N. S., *Phys. Rev.* 1942, **62**, 261.
2. HENSHAW, D. G., *Phys. Rev.* 1957, **105**, 976.
3. CORNER, J. and LENNARD-JONES, J. E., *Proc. roy. Soc.* 1941, **A178**, 401.
4. RUSHBROOKE, G. S., *Proc. roy. Soc. Edin.* 1940, **A60**, 182.
5. DAHLER, J. S., *J. chem. Phys.* 1958, **29**, 1082.
6. GREEN, H. S., *Handbuch der Physik* (Edited by FLÜGGE, S.), vol. 10, p. 48, Springer-Verlag, Berlin, 1960.
7. BARKER, J. A. To be published.

CHAPTER 11

QUANTUM EFFECTS

11.1 Classical and Quantum Theories of Liquids

The use of classical mechanics in the theory of liquids is an approximation which does not lead to serious error except for liquids of very low molecular weight (helium, hydrogen). However, even in the case of argon small but appreciable quantum corrections to the results given by the classical theory are required.

The quantum effects in liquids are of two kinds.[1] First there are "diffraction" or "uncertainty" effects which may be regarded as arising directly from the uncertainty principle. As we confine the molecules to smaller regions the uncertainty in the momentum must increase, so that the average kinetic energy rises. This is different from the situation in classical mechanics, where the average kinetic energy depends only on the temperature. This increase in kinetic energy gives rise to an increase in pressure over the classical value (at constant volume) or to an increase in volume (at constant pressure). The magnitude of this effect depends on the dimensionless parameter $h/\sigma(m\epsilon)^{1/2}$ which we shall denote by Λ^*. Here h is Planck's constant, m the molecular mass and σ and ϵ are characteristic intermolecular lengths and energies, respectively—for example the constants in the 12–6 potential.

One can see very simply why the parameter Λ^* is the significant one. If a molecule is confined to a region with length of order σ then the uncertainty in the velocity v is of order $h/m\sigma$, so that the minimum kinetic energy $\frac{1}{2}mv^2$ must be of order $h^2/m\sigma^2$. The importance of the quantum effect must depend on the ratio of this kinetic energy to the characteristic energy ϵ, i.e. on $h^2/\sigma^2 m\epsilon$ or Λ^{*2}. Alternatively one can characterize Λ^* as the ratio of the de Broglie wavelength for a system of reduced mass $m/2$ and energy to the characteristic length σ. This emphasizes the "diffraction" character of the quantum effect.

The second kind of quantum effect is the "symmetry" or "statistics" effect. This arises from the fact that the only permissible energy levels are those for which the wave function is antisymmetrical (for molecules obeying Fermi–Dirac statistics) or symmetrical (for molecules obeying Bose–Einstein statistics) in the interchange of any two molecules. Substances with antisymmetrical wave functions satisfy the Pauli exclusion principle, which states that no two molecules can occupy identical one-particle quantum states. This means that the presence of one molecule reduces the number of quantum states accessible to a second molecule in its neighbourhood, and this leads to an apparent repulsion between the molecules. Similarly for molecules obeying Bose–Einstein statistics the symmetry effect leads to an apparent attraction between the molecules. For a *perfect* Bose–Einstein gas this apparent attraction is associated with the "Bose–Einstein condensation", in which below a certain critical temperature all the molecules may "condense" into the lowest quantum state, and the volume approaches zero at a constant pressure. The λ-transition which occurs in liquid ^{4}He at 2·2°K is now generally regarded as being a phenomenon of this type, modified of course by the interactions between the molecules. This is a special problem which we shall not discuss further.

Apart from the special case of helium at low temperatures the symmetry effect is always very small, and we shall not discuss it in detail.

11.2 *Quantum Mechanics and Corresponding States*[2–4]

In section 1.4 we derived the classical principle of corresponding states, which may be stated in the form that for substances having the same potential function apart from scale factors of energy and length the reduced pressure $p\sigma^3/\epsilon$ is a universal function of the two reduced variables $V/N\sigma^3$ and kT/ϵ. This could have been derived on dimensional grounds since $V/N\sigma^3$ and kT/ϵ are the only dimensionless quantities that can be formed from combinations of V/N, σ, ϵ, kT and m. If now we pass to quantum mechanics we must consider also Planck's constant h. It then appears that there is a third independent dimensionless combination, namely $h/\sigma(m\epsilon)^{1/2}$ or Λ^*. Thus we should expect the quantum mechanical principle of corresponding states to take the form that $p\sigma^3/\epsilon$ is a universal function of the three variables $V/N\sigma^3$, kT/ϵ and Λ^*. Strictly speaking we should expect to find *different* universal functions for molecules obeying Fermi–Dirac and Bose–Einstein statistics. However, the differences are small except at very low temperatures. In fact de Boer and Lunbeck[4] predicted critical constants and vapour pressures for ^{3}He by extrapolating plots against Λ^* of the corresponding quantities for the substances listed in Table 11.1. Later measurements showed that these estimates were quite accurate, although ^{4}He and ^{3}He obey Bose–Einstein and Fermi–Dirac statistics respectively.

TABLE 11.1

Some values of Λ^* (from de Boer and Lunbeck[4])

Substance	Xe	Kr	A	N$_2$	Ne	H$_2$	^{4}He	^{3}He
Λ^*	0·064	0·102	0·187	0·225	0·591	1·73	2·64	3·05

To give an idea of the magnitude of the quantum effect we shall quote an estimate by de Boer and Lunbeck based on experimental data that the reduced liquid volume for $kT/\epsilon = 0.7$ is given approximately by

$$V/V_0 = 1\cdot2 + 0\cdot4\,\Lambda^{*2} \tag{11.2.1}$$

Thus for liquid argon at the triple point the quantum effect increases the volume by about 1 per cent, while the corresponding increase for neon is about 12 per cent. For hydrogen at $kT/\epsilon = 0\cdot7$ V_l/V_0 is about 2.2 while for helium at $kT/\epsilon = 0\cdot5$ it is 3·8.

11.3   *The Partition Function and Configuration Integral*

A correct quantal theory of liquids should be based on an evaluation of the partition function Z defined by equation (1.4.1). This would involve solving the Schrödinger equation for the whole set of molecules in order to determine the energy levels E_i. If the cell model is used the energy levels for the whole systems are sums of one-particle energies and the partition function factorizes to a product of one-particle partition functions, so that the calculation becomes feasible. We shall return to this later. If the approximation of using the cell model is not permissible the determination of the energy levels is not practicable. It is however possible to find an expansion of the partition function in powers of Planck's constant. The first term is just the classical result given by equation (1.4.3) and higher terms give quantum corrections. For substances of sufficiently high molecular weight the convergence of this series is quite satisfactory. We shall not give details of the derivation of this expansion, which is due to Kirkwood.[5] The result is[1]

$$Z = (2\pi m kT/h^2)^{3N/2}Q' \tag{11.3.1}$$

$$Q' = \frac{1}{N!}\int \ldots \int \exp\left(-U/kT\right)\left[1 + \lambda^2 \sum_j w_2^{(j)} + O(\lambda^4)\right.$$

$$\left. + O(\exp\{-2\pi R_{ij}^2/\lambda^2\})\right] dx_1 \ldots dz_N \tag{11.3.2}$$

$$w_2^{(j)} = -\frac{1}{24\pi kT} \left[\frac{\partial^2 U}{\partial x_j^2} + \frac{\partial^2 U}{\partial y_j^2} + \frac{\partial^2 U}{\partial z_j^2} \right]$$

$$+ \frac{1}{48\pi(kT)^2} \left[\left(\frac{\partial U}{\partial x_j}\right)^2 + \left(\frac{\partial U}{\partial y_j}\right)^2 + \left(\frac{\partial U}{\partial z_j}\right)^2 \right] \quad (11.3.3)$$

$$\lambda^2 = h^2/2\pi m kT \quad (11.3.4)$$

In (2) the notation $O(x)$ means "terms of the order of x". The terms of order $\exp(-2\pi R_{ij}^2/\lambda^2)$ are the terms arising from symmetry effects. Since the only important contributions to the integral in (2) come from regions of configuration space in which R_{ij} is roughly equal to or greater than σ, the exponential is of the same order as

$$\exp\left(-\frac{4\pi^2}{\varLambda^{*2}} \cdot \frac{kT}{\epsilon}\right)$$

or smaller. Except for helium this is a very small number indeed, for temperatures at which the liquid exists (cf. the values of $\varLambda^*$ in Table 11.1). It is this exponential dependence of the symmetry effects on $-1/\varLambda^{*2}$ which justifies their neglect for liquids other than helium.

The term of order λ^2 is the first quantum correction term. It can be evaluated by any method which can be used for evaluating the classical configuration integral. Thus equation (2) provides a method for extending the classical lattice theories to take account of quantum effects, provided that the quantum effects are small. Neglect of terms of order λ^4, λ^6, etc., is justified for all liquids except helium, deuterium and hydrogen.

11.4 Cell Theory; Small Quantum Effects

A calculation of the first and second quantum corrections (i.e. the terms of order $\varLambda^{*2}$ and $\varLambda^{*4}$) was made on the basis of the cell theory by de Boer and Lunbeck.[4] They used the modified form of the L-J-D theory with reduced coordination number which we have discussed at the end of section 4.5, and made calculations with the coordination number z chosen as 9 and 10. From the results they calculated the slope of a plot of the reduced liquid volume V/V_0 against $\varLambda^{*2}$, that is $dV_l^*/d\varLambda^{*2}$. The experimental value of this quantity is close to 0·41 in the temperature range from $kT/\epsilon = 0·7$ to $kT/\epsilon = 1·0$. The values calculated theoretically for $z = 10$ fell from 0·22 at $kT/\epsilon = 0·7$ to 0·13 at $kT/\epsilon = 1·0$. These values are roughly of the right magnitude although the agreement is quantitatively unsatisfactory. We have already seen that this modification of the L-J-D theory cannot be regarded as a satisfactory classical theory, so it is perhaps not surprising that the predicted results for the quantum effects are not in good quantitative agreement with experiment.

This theory would of course be correctly applied to *solid* inert gases if the co-ordination number 12 were used. Unfortunately de Boer and Lunbeck did not make calculations for this value of z, which would be of considerable interest. A linear extrapolation of the results of de Boer and Lunbeck for $z = 9$ and 10 to $z = 12$ would indicate a value of $dV_s^*/d\Lambda^{*2}$ close to 0·12 at $kT/\epsilon = 0·7$. On this basis the quantum correction would increase the calculated L-J-D value for the volume of solid argon from 1·037 V_0 (see Table 4.4) to 1·041 V_0. We have insufficient data to estimate the effect on the energy and entropy.

11.5   *Cell Theory; Large Quantum Effects*

The convergence of the expansion in powers of Λ^{*2} discussed above is good for neon and substances of higher molecular weight, doubtful for hydrogen and deuterium, and probably unsatisfactory for helium. Thus for hydrogen, deuterium and helium there is considerable interest in a direct evaluation of the quantum mechanical cell partition function. Recently Levelt and Hurst[6] have made exact calculations of the quantized energy levels (and of the partition function) for hydrogen and deuterium molecules moving in the L-J-D cell potential energy field. All energy levels with energies up to about 60ϵ were calculated for the single volume $V/V_0 = 5/3$. The partition function was then evaluated for kT/ϵ between 0·5 and 5·0. The determination of the energy levels involved extensive electronic computing. From the results it was possible to derive values for the energy, entropy and heat capacity. These differed substantially from the values calculated with the classical L-J-D theory. Because the energy levels and partition function were calculated only for a single volume it was not possible to determine the pressure.

Because the exact calculation of the partition function involves extensive computations a simpler approximate treatment is of considerable value. Hamann[7,8] has given a treatment of this kind, based on approximating the L-J-D field by a suitably chosen "square-well" potential. Hamann first made calculations for a "spherical square-well" potential, in which the potential energy was taken to be constant (equal to its value at the cell centre) when the distance ρ from the cell centre was less than a certain value ρ_1, and infinite when ρ was greater than ρ_1. The radius ρ_1 was chosen as the distance at which the L-J-D potential $\psi(\rho)$ was equal to zero, since $\psi(\rho)$ increases rapidly beyond this point. Even with this potential the evaluation of the partition function is laborious and Hamann made the further approximation of replacing the *sphere* of radius ρ_1 by a *cube* of the same volume. The Schrödinger equation then becomes separable and the evaluation of the partition function is comparatively simple. The partition function is given approximately by

$$ Z = \left[\frac{(2\pi m k T)^{1/2}}{h} \left(\frac{4\pi \rho_1^3}{3} \right)^{1/3} - \frac{1}{2} \right]^{3N} \exp\left(-U_0/kT \right) \quad (11.5.1) $$

This equation is a good approximation provided[9] that the first term in the square bracket is greater than 0·7 (when this term is 0·7 the error is 6 per cent and when it is 0·75 the error is 1·5 per cent).

The classical partition function is given by

$$ Z_{cl} = \left(\frac{2\pi m k T}{h^2} \right)^{3N/2} \left(\frac{4\pi \rho_1^3}{3} \right)^{N} \exp\left(-U_0/kT \right) \quad (11.5.2) $$

Thus the quantum correction to the free energy is given by

$$ \Delta A = -kT \ln (Z/Z_{cl}) $$

$$ = 3NkT \ln \left[\frac{9 \cdot 0710 y^{*1/2}\ T^{*1/2}\ V^{*1/3}\ \Lambda^{*-1}}{9 \cdot 0710 y^{*1/2}\ T^{*1/2}\ V^{*1/3} \Lambda^{*-1} - 1} \right] \quad (11.5.3) $$

In (3) T^* and V^* denote kT/ϵ and $V/N\sigma^3$, respectively, while $y^{*1/2}$ is the ratio of ρ_1 to the nearest-neighbour distance a. For given volume y^* is determined from the equation

$$ (1 + 12y^* + 25 \cdot 2\, y^{*2} + 12y^{*3} + y^{*4})(1 + y^*)^{-1}(1 - y^*)^{-6} - 2V^{*2} = 0 $$
$$ (11.5.4) $$

The quantum corrections to the energy, entropy and pressure can be calculated by differentiating equation (3) with respect to temperature and volume.

Hamann showed that the quantum corrections calculated from these equations were of about the right magnitude to explain the difference between the actual critical temperatures of hydrogen, deuterium, helium and neon and the values predicted on the basis of the classical L-J-D theory. Furthermore calculated pressure–volume isotherms for gaseous helium, hydrogen and deuterium at high pressures were in good agreement with experiment, in marked contrast with isotherms derived from the classical L-J-D theory.

Thus equations (1)–(4) provide a useful method for estimating quantum corrections on the basis of the cell theory. They should not, however, be used[9] when Λ^* is less than about 0·3. In this region the approximation of replacing the actual cell field by a square-well potential is unsatisfactory, and leads to the incorrect result that the quantum correction is proportional to Λ^* rather than the correct Λ^{*2}.

REFERENCES

1. HIRSCHFELDER, J. O., CURTISS, C. F. and BIRD, R. B., *Molecular Theory of Gases and Liquids*, ch. 6, by DE BOER, J. and BIRD, R. B., Chapman & Hall, London, 1954.
2. DE BOER, J., *Physica* 1948, **14**, 139.
3. DE BOER, J. and BLAISSE, B. S., *Physica* 1948, **14**, 149.
4. DE BOER, J. and LUNBECK, R. J., *Physica* 1948, **14**, 510, 520.
5. KIRKWOOD, J. G., *Phys. Rev.* 1933, **44**, 31.
6. LEVELT, J. M. H. and HURST, R. P., *J. chem. Phys.* 1960, **32**, 96.
7. HAMANN, S. D., *Trans. Faraday Soc.* 1952, **48**, 303.
8. DAVID, H. G. and HAMANN, S. D., *Trans. Faraday Soc.* 1953, **49**, 711.
9. HAMANN, S. D., Personal Communication.

CHAPTER 12

CONCLUSIONS, AND FURTHER PROBLEMS

12.1   *Present State of the Theory*

We have surveyed the various lattice theories of fluids, considering in detail their application to the simple fluid argon. It remains only to summarize our conclusions as to the present state of the theory of fluids, and to indicate briefly the problems presented by fluids in which the molecular interactions are more complicated.

Apart from the direct numerical methods of chapter 2 (Monte Carlo, molecular dynamics), which have their own inherent limitations, none of the theories which we have discussed can be regarded as entirely satisfactory. The cell theory in the form due to Lennard-Jones and Devonshire is essentially a theory of *solids*. If this theory is to be modified to describe liquids as well as solids then a satisfactory method of dealing with the problem of the communal entropy must be developed. Methods so far developed are adequate at comparatively low densities but inadequate at high densities; it seems certain that the communal entropy is important even in liquids at their triple points. A possible method of attack on this problem is mentioned at the end of chapter 6.

We have seen that attempts to base the L-J-D theory on a variational principle and to use the variational principle to improve the cell theory led to unsatisfactory results (chapter 5). The widely-held view that the justification for the L-J-D theory lies in Kirkwood's variational theory is incorrect. The true justification for the L-J-D approach lies in the fact that *correlation* effects are small, and the best way to improve the L-J-D theory is to allow for the correlation and communal effects (chapters 6 and 7).

Attempts to improve the L-J-D theory by allowing for the presence of empty cells ("hole" theories) give disappointing results (chapter 8). At present it seems that the rather doubtful gains associated with introducing empty cells are more than offset by the increased complexity of the theory. In this connection, however, one should bear in mind the remarkable (if semi-empirical) success of the order–disorder theory of melting described in section 3.4. In this theory the number of holes is rather arbitrarily taken to be equal to the number of molecules.

The tunnel theory (chapter 9) has not yet been investigated as fully as the cell theory. It gives calculated values of pressure and energy which are in good agreement with experiment, but the calculated entropies are less satisfactory. At present this is perhaps the most promising of the lattice theories. In the long run it seems likely that both the cell theory and the tunnel theory can be developed to give a satisfactory theory of fluids. Which of these theories will be easier to use cannot at present be decided.

At this point it seems appropriate to give some indication of the present relative status of the distribution function theories and lattice theories. The only explicit results available from distribution function theories are derived from the integral equations of Kirkwood and Born and Green, which are based on the "superposition approximation" expressing the triplet distribution function in terms of the pair distribution function. These equations have been solved for rigid spherical molecules[1] and for molecules interacting according to a modified 12–6 potential.[2,3] The unknown effect of the modification of the potential precludes a comparison of the latter results with experiment. However the results for rigid spherical molecules have been compared with results of Monte Carlo calculations and the agreement is found to be unsatisfactory at high densities.[4]

Thus the available evidence suggests that this kind of theory is not satisfactory for liquids. In the absence of detailed calculations it is impossible to predict whether a more sophisticated distribution function theory will be satisfactory. It seems to the present author that a satisfactory theory of the liquid state must involve in some way a detailed description of the *structure* of the liquid. But the pair distribution function does *not* describe the structure in detail, since many different three-dimensional structures may correspond to the same radial distribution function. Thus it seems that any theory which attempts to describe liquids in terms of pair and perhaps triplet distribution functions is placing a very great strain on the mathematics. This is a statement of personal opinion.

12.2 *Further Problems*

The theoretical developments that we have described have been based on the assumption that the mutual potential energy of two molecules depends only on the distance between their centres. This assumption can be exactly true only for inert gases. We now review briefly the attempts that have been made to describe theoretically the properties of liquids with more complicated molecules.

For molecules which are far from spherical there is no satisfactory detailed theory and no general agreement on the detailed nature of the interaction between molecules. The properties of solutions containing long-chain molecules, in particular polymer molecules, are often discussed in terms of a very simple lattice model[5] in which the molecules occupy connected sets of sites on a lattice. In this model the entropy of the solution is related to the number of geometrically possible ways of arranging the molecules on the lattice. Prigogine et al.[6] combined this with the cell theory approach in an attempt to develop a cell theory for chain molecules, considered as chains of units interacting according to a 12–6 potential.

For molecules which are nearly spherical some progress has been made. For "globular" molecules such as CF_4 and SF_6 it is a good approximation to neglect the non-spherical interactions altogether. The only effect of the polyatomic nature of the molecules then is to change the potential energy function from that appropriate for monatomic liquids. Hamann and Lambert[7,8] found that a 28–7 potential was more appropriate for globular molecules than the 12–6 potential, and they made calculations using the L-J-D theory for the former potential.

For less symmetrical molecules it is not permissible to neglect the non-spherical nature altogether. However, it is possible to find useful results by treating the non-spherical part of the interaction as a perturbation. A convenient summary of this kind of work is given by Rowlinson.[9]

Highly polar and "associated" liquids present special difficulties, because the molecular interactions depend strongly on the orientations of the molecules. Pople[10] has described a cell theory for polar liquids, but this theory can be expected to be valid only when the polarity is weak. Simple lattice models for solutions containing associated liquids have been described,[11] but these models are too simple to be useful in interpreting the properties of pure liquids. Probably liquids such as alcohols whose molecules form intermolecular hydrogen bonds are best pictured in terms of a chemical equilibrium between monomers, dimers and higher molecular aggregates. An interesting theory of the structure of water, whose molecules are completely linked by hydrogen bonds, has been given by Pople.[12]

12.3 *Conclusion*

For simple fluids such as inert gases the interactions between the molecules are comparatively well understood. The statistical theory which relates the molecular interactions to macroscopic properties cannot be regarded as altogether satisfactory, but the foundations upon which a satisfactory theory can be developed are laid. For liquids with complicated molecules, in particular for highly polar and associated liquids, a great deal of work will be required before the molecular interactions are properly understood. For this reason development of detailed statistical theories relating molecular interactions with macroscopic properties in such liquids has hardly begun.

REFERENCES

1. KIRKWOOD, J. G., MAUN, E. K. and ALDER, B. J., *J. chem. Phys.* 1950, **18**, 1040.
2. KIRKWOOD, J. G., LEWINSON, V. A. and ALDER, B. J., *J. chem. Phys.* 1952, **20**, 929.
3. ZWANZIG, R. W., KIRKWOOD, J. G., STRIPP, K. F. and OPPENHEIM, I., *J. chem. Phys.* 1953, **21**, 1268; 1954, **22**, 1625.
4. WOOD, W. W. and JACOBSON, J. D., *J. chem. Phys.* 1957, **27**, 1207.
5. GUGGENHAIM, E. A., *Mixtures*, chs. X–XII, Oxford University Press, 1952.
6. PRIGOGINE, I., TRAPPENIERS, N. and MATHOT, V., *Dis. Faraday Soc.* 1953, **15**, 93.
7. HAMANN, S. D. and LAMBERT, J. A., *Aust. J. Chem.* 1954, **7**, 1, 18, 219.
8. HAMANN, S. D., *Aust. J. Chem.* 1955, 8, 21.
9. ROWLINSON, J. S., *Liquids and Liquid Mixtures*, chs. 7 and 8, Butterworths, London, 1959.
10. POPLE, J. A., *Proc. roy. Soc.* 1952, **A215**, 67.
11. BARKER, J. A. and SMITH, F., *J. chem. Phys.* 1954, **22**, 375.
12. POPLE, J. A., *Proc. roy. Soc.* 1952, **A205**, 163.

AUTHOR INDEX

SUBJECT INDEX